ESSENTIAL SKILLS IN MATHS

Answer Book

BOOK 2

Nelson

Graham Newman and Ron Bull

National Curriculum coverage

Book	1	2	3	4	5
Levels	3–4	4–5	5–6	6–7	7–8

Thomas Nelson and Sons Ltd
Nelson House   Mayfield Road
Walton-on-Thames   Surrey
KT12 5PL   UK

© R. Bull, G. Newman 1996

First published by Thomas Nelson and Sons Ltd 1996

I(T)P Thomas Nelson is an International Thomson Publishing Company.

I(T)P is used under licence.

ISBN 0-17-431464-7
NPN 9 8 7 6 5 4 3

Printed in China

Contents

SHAPE, SPACE AND MEASURES

HANDLING DATA

Number

1 MENTAL ARITHMETIC: ADDING AND SUBTRACTING TWO 2-DIGIT NUMBERS WITHOUT A CALCULATOR

Exercise 1A

1 71	**2** 55	**3** 83	**4** 50
5 89	**6** 76	**7** 89	**8** 73
9 42	**10** 65	**11** 88	**12** 99
13 96	**14** 44	**15** 7	**16** 74
17 41	**18** 88	**19** 21	**20** 52
21 22	**22** 105	**23** 108	**24** 102
25 37	**26** 96	**27** 7	**28** 126
29 65	**30** 32		

Exercise 1B

1 95	**2** 12	**3** 14	**4** 77
5 103	**6** 25	**7** 55	**8** 96
9 84	**10** 16	**11** 59	**12** 97
13 42	**14** 83	**15** 95	**16** 42
17 101	**18** 21	**19** 28	**20** 95
21 38	**22** 95	**23** 78	**24** 96
25 102	**26** 42	**27** 18	**28** 115
29 31	**30** 120		

2 ADDING AND SUBTRACTING TWO 3-DIGIT NUMBERS WITHOUT A CALCULATOR

Exercise 2A

1 597	**2** 585	**3** 114	**4** 503
5 687	**6** 853	**7** 471	**8** 213
9 190	**10** 97	**11** 654	**12** 807
13 326	**14** 497	**15** 399	**16** 69
17 397	**18** 168	**19** 207	**20** 674
21 262	**22** 153	**23** 731	**24** 326
25 996	**26** 90	**27** 207	**28** 813
29 509	**30** 823		

Exercise 2B

1 567	**2** 887	**3** 568	**4** 271
5 411	**6** 156	**7** 953	**8** 909
9 69	**10** 191	**11** 82	**12** 792
13 707	**14** 317	**15** 519	**16** 182
17 823	**18** 205	**19** 387	**20** 482
21 922	**22** 783	**23** 110	**24** 1000
25 292	**26** 177	**27** 382	**28** 774
29 964	**30** 871		

3 ADDING AND SUBTRACTING SEVERAL 1-DIGIT NUMBERS WITHOUT A CALCULATOR

Exercise 3A

1 21	**2** 20	**3** 14	**4** 21
5 18	**6** 18	**7** 22	**8** 19
9 22	**10** 21	**11** 6	**12** 6
13 5	**14** 14	**15** 6	**16** 1
17 8	**18** 6	**19** 11	**20** 13
21 13	**22** 5	**23** 7	**24** 19
25 16	**26** 22	**27** 7	**28** 24
29 6	**30** 15		

Exercise 3B

1 15	**2** 18	**3** 17	**4** 16
5 19	**6** 15	**7** 18	**8** 20
9 22	**10** 21	**11** 12	**12** 11
13 12	**14** 11	**15** 8	**16** 3
17 14	**18** 9	**19** 4	**20** 13
21 14	**22** 12	**23** 5	**24** 25
25 22	**26** 8	**27** 10	**28** 3
29 13	**30** 9		

4 NUMBERS TO WORDS

Exercise 4A

1 Two thousand, five hundred
2 One thousand, eight hundred and sixty-three
3 Nine thousand and five
4 Ten thousand and five
5 Eleven thousand, nine hundred and ninety-eight
6 Ninety-one thousand, two hundred and fifty
7 Fifty-five thousand, five hundred and six
8 Thirty-two thousand and twenty-five
9 Seventy-four thousand, two hundred and eighty-eight
10 Twenty-six thousand, two hundred and ninety-three
11 Fifteen thousand
12 Fifty-five thousand and fifty-five
13 Eighty-seven thousand, six hundred and sixty
14 Forty thousand and ten

15 One hundred and eighty thousand, three hundred and nine
16 Five hundred and fifty-nine thousand
17 Nine hundred and ninety-nine thousand
18 Two hundred and eighty-one thousand and thirty
19 Ninety thousand and fifty-four
20 Seven hundred and fifty thousand and ten
21 Three million, five hundred and eighty-eight thousand
22 Seven hundred and fifty-eight thousand, eight hundred and sixty
23 Twenty-one million
24 Five million, five hundred thousand
25 Eight hundred and twelve thousand
26 Six million, one hundred thousand and eight
27 Eighty million
28 Five hundred and forty million
29 Ten million, two hundred and fifty thousand
30 Twenty-six million and twenty

Exercise 4B

1 One thousand, five hundred
2 Seven thousand, nine hundred and thirty-four
3 Two thousand, six hundred and fifty
4 Thirty-five thousand, six hundred and ninety
5 Fourteen thousand, six hundred
6 Eighty-six thousand, one hundred
7 Thirteen thousand, two hundred and forty-two
8 Twenty-seven thousand, two hundred
9 Fifty thousand and one
10 Nineteen thousand and two
11 Twelve thousand, five hundred and fifty
12 Ten thousand, five hundred and sixty-seven
13 Sixty-five thousand, eight hundred and sixty-two
14 One hundred and nineteen thousand, six hundred and sixty-three
15 Three hundred and ninety-six thousand, five hundred
16 Two hundred and forty-five thousand
17 Three hundred and thirty thousand
18 Six hundred and thirty-one thousand, eight hundred and sixty-six
19 Four hundred and ninety thousand
20 Nine hundred and fifty thousand and fifty
21 One million and one
22 Nine million, one hundred thousand
23 Five million, sixty thousand and five
24 Seven million, eight hundred and seventy-nine thousand, four hundred
25 Fifty-five million

26 Fourteen million, five hundred thousand
27 Nine hundred million
28 Eight-five million
29 Forty million, five hundred thousand
30 Thirteen million, five hundred

5 WORDS TO NUMBERS

Exercise 5A

1	5001	2	1942	3	31 000
4	87 200	5	27 750	6	20 005
7	83 270	8	100 300	9	299 990
10	773 008	11	434 630	12	195 210
13	123 520	14	897 000	15	8 561 000
16	20 000 000	17	2 150 000	18	99 910 000
19	650 000 000	20	1 000 085		

Exercise 5B

1	9548	2	4135	3	38 500
4	14 002	5	53 312	6	82 767
7	15 444	8	49 070	9	30 455
10	21 090	11	61 700	12	305 000
13	400 000	14	13 850	15	370 689
16	11 500	17	67 500 000	18	6 800 013
19	750 000 000	20	101 000 000		

6 TABLES: TO 10 × 10

Exercise 6A

1	25	2	18	3	20	4	21	5	15
6	18	7	18	8	24	9	20	10	27
11	24	12	15	13	24	14	35	15	36
16	21	17	70	18	16	19	28	20	30
21	50	22	32	23	36	24	27	25	35
26	24	27	14	28	45	29	48	30	30
31	32	32	42	33	40	34	48	35	45
36	56	37	54	38	56	39	54	40	40
41	63	42	49	43	12	44	90	45	36
46	28	47	72	48	42	49	64	.50	63
51	30	52	24	53	27	54	24	55	28
56	40	57	32	58	42	59	24	60	30
61	32	62	35	63	45	64	36	65	20
66	21	67	15	68	54	69	50	70	25
71	18	72	36	73	60	74	49	75	72
76	63	77	70	78	48	79	16	80	45
81	14	82	36	83	64	84	42	85	18
86	80	87	28	88	56	89	18	90	63
91	72	92	21	93	54	94	40	95	27
96	48	97	35	98	56	99	24	100	81

Exercise 6B

1 18	**2** 15	**3** 12	**4** 25	**5** 12
6 20	**7** 21	**8** 42	**9** 10	**10** 16
11 24	**12** 28	**13** 45	**14** 32	**15** 30
16 28	**17** 30	**18** 24	**19** 50	**20** 21
21 20	**22** 27	**23** 24	**24** 16	**25** 36
26 48	**27** 35	**28** 15	**29** 36	**30** 18
31 12	**32** 24	**33** 40	**34** 36	**35** 56
36 72	**37** 30	**38** 64	**39** 18	**40** 49
41 72	**42** 35	**43** 32	**44** 48	**45** 45
46 32	**47** 54	**48** 63	**49** 42	**50** 60
51 72	**52** 63	**53** 80	**54** 54	**55** 27
56 56	**57** 40	**58** 36	**59** 60	**60** 50
61 28	**62** 21	**63** 25	**64** 12	**65** 20
66 15	**67** 24	**68** 50	**69** 21	**70** 18
71 20	**72** 24	**73** 35	**74** 16	**75** 70
76 45	**77** 32	**78** 30	**79** 28	**80** 54
81 54	**82** 56	**83** 30	**84** 24	**85** 42
86 36	**87** 48	**88** 27	**89** 48	**90** 35
91 81	**92** 40	**93** 49	**94** 72	**95** 56
96 36	**97** 63	**98** 64	**99** 42	**100** 63

7 MULTIPLICATION AND DIVISION BY A 1-DIGIT NUMBER WITHOUT A CALCULATOR

Exercice 7A

1 36	**2** 111	**3** 26	**4** 144
5 8	**6** 23	**7** 65	**8** 176
9 84	**10** 38	**11** 5	**12** 231
13 194	**14** 104	**15** 16	**16** 30
17 375	**18** 6	**19** 136	**20** 58
21 15	**22** 15	**23** 156	**24** 9
25 12	**26** 357	**27** 416	**28** 6
29 26	**30** 408		

Exercice 7B

1 15	**2** 16	**3** 54	**4** 195
5 95	**6** 41	**7** 7	**8** 19
9 174	**10** 235	**11** 42	**12** 11
13 8	**14** 12	**15** 147	**16** 456
17 465	**18** 356	**19** 16	**20** 12
21 15	**22** 8	**23** 75	**24** 369
25 78	**26** 301	**27** 14	**28** 13
29 658	**30** 318		

Exercice 7C

1 196	**2** 224	**3** 25	**4** 12
5 114	**6** 117	**7** 70	**8** 552
9 120	**10** 261	**11** 30	**12** 16
13 45	**14** 28	**15** 49	**16** 152
17 639	**18** 234	**19** 360	**20** 22
21 80	**22** 25	**23** 207	**24** 252
25 632	**26** 588	**27** 40	**28** 35
29 15	**30** 360		

Exercise 7D

1 486	**2** 172	**3** 183	**4** 80
5 292	**6** 231	**7** 819	**8** 55
9 558	**10** 25	**11** 65	**12** 248
13 52	**14** 432	**15** 149	**16** 536
17 57	**18** 37	**19** 222	**20** 306
21 91	**22** 217	**23** 415	**24** 510
25 14	**26** 23	**27** 380	**28** 67
29 959	**30** 2848		

8 MULTIPLYING AND DIVIDING BY POWERS OF 10

Exercise 8A

1 300	**2** 7000	**3** 1100	**4** 12
5 37	**6** 200	**7** 320	**8** 71 000
9 45	**10** 301	**11** 680	**12** 6000
13 2900	**14** 80	**15** 75	**16** 278
17 17 200	**18** 9100	**19** 5000	**20** 830
21 52	**22** 2700	**23** 8500	**24** 4000
25 7000	**26** 150	**27** 4500	**28** 13 000
29 97	**30** 11		

Exercise 8B

1 90	**2** 17 000	**3** 6500	**4** 3
5 40	**6** 7800	**7** 8400	**8** 16 000
9 4030	**10** 56	**11** 63	**12** 4820
13 18 000	**14** 63 200	**15** 440	**16** 970
17 180	**18** 31	**19** 2600	**20** 30 600
21 800 000	**22** 5000	**23** 190	**24** 506
25 2000	**26** 570 000	**27** 600	**28** 51
29 73 300	**30** 75 000 000		

9 MULTIPLICATION BY A 2-DIGIT NUMBER WITHOUT A CALCULATOR

Exercise 9A

1 1166	**2** 1846	**3** 2772
4 4710	**5** 1568	**6** 4236
7 1417	**8** 2800	**9** 5656
10 1768	**11** 8192	**12** 3611
13 8967	**14** 7854	**15** 10 880
16 14 117	**17** 6894	**18** 18 952
19 15 792	**20** 51 606	**21** 18 625
22 7106	**23** 17 732	**24** 33 867
25 50 985	**26** 74 368	**27** 30 586
28 33 176	**29** 83 629	**30** 29 155

Exercise 9B

1 1625		**2** 1276		**3** 1740	
4 3094		**5** 1989		**6** 4725	
7 2112		**8** 2982		**9** 8096	
10 6945		**11** 9262		**12** 4284	
13 3726		**14** 10 400		**15** 8343	
16 5642		**17** 20 576		**18** 29 028	
19 49 042		**20** 19 425		**21** 9050	
22 31 960		**23** 24 975		**24** 45 441	
25 12 814		**26** 46 308		**27** 30 008	
28 66 608		**29** 43 239		**30** 45 927	

10 DIVISION BY A 2-DIGIT NUMBER WITHOUT A CALCULATOR

Exercise 10A

1 13	**2** 13	**3** 9	**4** 15	**5** 15
6 12	**7** 11	**8** 6	**9** 11	**10** 12
11 17	**12** 13	**13** 7	**14** 9	**15** 12
16 6	**17** 12	**18** 13	**19** 15	**20** 33
21 29	**22** 13	**23** 6	**24** 11	**25** 14
26 6	**27** 4	**28** 4	**29** 7	**30** 15

Exercise 10B

1 14	**2** 24	**3** 15	**4** 16	**5** 11
6 13	**7** 11	**8** 35	**9** 9	**10** 13
11 11	**12** 12	**13** 11	**14** 7	**15** 12
16 11	**17** 15	**18** 11	**19** 13	**20** 13
21 18	**22** 19	**23** 31	**24** 28	**25** 25
26 6	**27** 8	**28** 15	**29** 19	**30** 11

11 SIMPLE FACTORS

Exercises 11A and 11C

1 2 × 8, 4 × 4
2 2 × 15, 5 × 6
3 2 × 22, 4 × 11
4 2 × 30, 3 × 20, 4 × 15, 5 × 12, 6 × 10
5 2 × 10, 4 × 5
6 2 × 39, 3 × 26, 6 × 13
7 5 × 13
8 2 × 23
9 3 × 5
10 2 × 18, 3 × 12, 4 × 9, 6 × 6
11 2 × 25, 5 × 10
12 2 × 42, 3 × 28, 4 × 21, 6 × 14, 7 × 12
13 3 × 19
14 2 × 14, 4 × 7
15 2 × 43
16 5 × 25
17 2 × 54, 3 × 36, 4 × 27, 6 × 18, 9 × 12
18 3 × 31
19 2 × 36, 3 × 24, 4 × 18, 6 × 12, 8 × 9
20 2 × 31
21 2 × 60, 3 × 40, 4 × 30, 5 × 24, 6 × 20, 8 × 15, 10 × 12
22 2 × 45, 3 × 30, 5 × 18, 6 × 15, 9 × 10
23 3 × 21, 7 × 9
24 3 × 35, 5 × 21, 7 × 15
25 2 × 72, 3 × 48, 4 × 36, 6 × 24, 8 × 18, 9 × 16, 12 × 12
26 2 × 57, 3 × 38, 6 × 19
27 2 × 33, 3 × 22, 6 × 11
28 2 × 68, 4 × 34, 8 × 17
29 3 × 23
30 2 × 125, 5 × 50, 10 × 25

Exercises 11B and 11D

1 2 × 9, 3 × 6
2 2 × 4
3 2 × 21, 3 × 14, 6 × 7
4 2 × 29
5 2 × 6, 3 × 4
6 2 × 16, 4 × 8
7 2 × 26, 4 × 13
8 2 × 12, 3 × 8, 4 × 6
9 2 × 40, 4 × 20, 5 × 16, 8 × 10
10 2 × 34, 4 × 17
11 2 × 24, 3 × 16, 4 × 12, 6 × 8
12 2 × 50, 4 × 25, 5 × 20, 10 × 10
13 2 × 20, 4 × 10, 5 × 8
14 3 × 17
15 2 × 32, 4 × 16, 8 × 8
16 2 × 41
17 2 × 28, 4 × 14, 7 × 8
18 3 × 27, 9 × 9
19 2 × 27, 3 × 18, 6 × 9
20 3 × 29
21 2 × 75, 3 × 50, 5 × 30, 6 × 25, 10 × 15
22 2 × 55, 5 × 22, 10 × 11
23 5 × 19
24 2 × 35, 5 × 14, 7 × 10
25 2 × 56, 4 × 28, 7 × 16, 8 × 14
26 2 × 53
27 2 × 62, 4 × 31
28 2 × 80, 4 × 40, 8 × 20, 10 × 16, 32 × 5
29 5 × 23
30 2 × 66, 3 × 44, 4 × 33, 6 × 22, 11 × 12

12 THE VALUE OF A GIVEN DIGIT WITHIN A NUMBER

Exercise 12A

1 20 000, 100
2 5000, 300
3 600 000, 50 000
4 3000, 50
5 90 000, 400
6 800, 90
7 500 000, 6
8 2 000 000, 60 000
9 3 000 000, 500 000
10 5000, 80
11 10 000, 600
12 5 000 000, 60
13 10 000 000, 2 000 000
14 20 000, 600
15 3 000 000, 50 000
16 Twenty thousand, six hundred
17 Three thousand, eighty
18 One hundred thousand, four hundred
19 Two hundred thousand, five thousand
20 Nine hundred thousand, eighty thousand
21 One million, fifty thousand
22 Ten thousand, four
23 Five hundred thousand, three hundred
24 Twenty million, one million
25 Two thousand, six hundred
26 Ninety thousand, seventy
27 Three million, ten thousand
28 Ten million, seven million
29 Ten thousand, twenty
30 Seven million, five hundred thousand

Exercise 12B

1 9 000, 700
2 20 000, 40
3 20 000, 5000
4 700 000, 100
5 10 000, 3000
6 4 000 000, 600 000
7 100 000, 5000
8 8000, 500
9 10 000 000, 1 000 000
10 5000, 70
11 20 000, 400
12 5 000 000, 30 000
13 200 000 000, 5 000 000
14 10 000, 8
15 2 000 000, 50 000

16 Ten thousand, forty
17 Six thousand, four hundred
18 Five hundred thousand, six thousand
19 Seventy thousand, one thousand
20 Eight thousand, fifty
21 Twenty thousand, one
22 Eight million, nine hundred thousand
23 Sixty thousand, one hundred
24 Sixty thousand, five thousand
25 Four hundred thousand, three thousand
26 Forty million, five million
27 One hundred thousand, eight thousand
28 Six million, seven thousand
29 Fifty thousand, three hundred
30 Five million, four hundred thousand

13 ESTIMATING THE ANSWERS TO ADDITIONS AND SUBTRACTIONS

(The actual answers to the calculations are given.)

Exercise 13A

1 387	2 301	3 55	4 67
5 561	6 254	7 25	8 83
9 200	10 103	11 547	12 871
13 631	14 1425	15 267	16 1138
17 820	18 1103	19 1144	20 325

Exercise 13B

1 165	2 69	3 421	4 330
5 114	6 345	7 419	8 276
9 109	10 687	11 655	12 225
13 344	14 1166	15 783	16 337
17 2252	18 747	19 1802	20 107

14 DIVISION AND MULTIPLICATION AS INVERSE OPERATIONS WITH AND WITHOUT A CALCULATOR

Exercise 14A

1 J	2 M	3 D	4 A	5 C
6 G	7 N	8 F	9 O	10 P
11 H	12 T	13 E	14 B	15 R
16 L	17 Q	18 I	19 K	20 S

Exercise 14B

1 K	2 P	3 C	4 E	5 A
6 N	7 G	8 S	9 R	10 L
11 D	12 H	13 J	14 O	15 I
16 B	17 M	18 F	19 T	20 Q

Exercise 14C

1 E	**2** M	**3** P	**4** B	**5** N
6 L	**7** A	**8** Q	**9** H	**10** K
11 C	**12** T	**13** F	**14** O	**15** I
16 S	**17** J	**18** R	**19** D	**20** G

Exercise 14D

1 B	**2** M	**3** F	**4** R	**5** L
6 A	**7** S	**8** G	**9** P	**10** J
11 T	**12** D	**13** O	**14** K	**15** H
16 Q	**17** N	**18** E	**19** I	**20** C

15 DIVISION TO THE NEAREST WHOLE NUMBER WITH AND WITHOUT A CALCULATOR

Exercise 15A

1 6	**2** 5	**3** 7	**4** 5	**5** 8
6 11	**7** 5	**8** 7	**9** 8	**10** 7
11 9	**12** 16	**13** 11	**14** 10	**15** 4
16 6	**17** 3	**18** 17	**19** 10	**20** 4

Exercise 15B

1 7	**2** 13	**3** 13	**4** 11	**5** 11
6 3	**7** 5	**8** 6	**9** 7	**10** 12
11 3	**12** 11	**13** 4	**14** 11	**15** 6
16 12	**17** 8	**18** 15	**19** 13	**20** 10

Exercise 15C

1 21	**2** 22	**3** 17	**4** 27	**5** 13
6 20	**7** 17	**8** 36	**9** 26	**10** 48
11 63	**12** 121	**13** 27	**14** 15	**15** 76
16 24	**17** 30	**18** 59	**19** 29	**20** 60

Exercise 15D

1 24	**2** 17	**3** 19	**4** 51	**5** 23
6 35	**7** 96	**8** 28	**9** 9	**10** 13
11 21	**12** 172	**13** 29	**14** 19	**15** 56
16 775	**17** 94	**18** 208	**19** 45	**20** 162

16 PROBLEMS INVOLVING ADDITION, SUBTRACTION, MULTIPLICATION AND DIVISION WITHOUT A CALCULATOR

Exercise 16A

1 300 cm	**2** 19 cm	**3** 24 min
4 12 g	**5** £3.75	**6** £12.49
7 15	**8** 288	**9** 105
10 7	**11** £56	**12** £12.74
13 £15.48	**14** 1320 ml	**15** 13
16 135°	**17** 792	**18** 95
19 324	**20** 362	

Exercise 16B

1 23	**2** 91 m	**3** 8
4 240 min	**5** 70	**6** 17
7 8 cm	**8** £20	**9** 216
10 £9.50	**11** 216	**12** 28
13 240	**14** 49	**15** 127
16 55	**17** 144	**18** 270
19 343	**20** 107	

17 PROBLEMS INVOLVING ADDITION, SUBTRACTION, MULTIPLICATION AND DIVISION WITH A CALCULATOR

Exercise 17A

1 330	**2** 390	**3** 16
4 165	**5** 85	**6** £498.58
7 12	**8** £208.79	**9** 24
10 £3.36	**11** 504	**12** 233 km
13 £74.84	**14** 7	**15** 276
16 8	**17** 336	**18** £160.31
19 1827	**20** 9	

Exercise 17B

1 £142.85	**2** 12	**3** £71.84
4 £53.38	**5** 24491	**6** 7
7 £42.95	**8** 235 ml	
9 No (total = 1050 kg)		**10** £193.08
11 26	**12** 187 km	**13** 156
14 £94.19	**15** 13	
16 1330 cm or 13.3 m		**17** 330 h
18 240	**19** 120	**20** 167

REVISION

Exercise A

1 (a) 61 (b) 38 (c) 39 (d) 53
2 (a) 8 (b) 1 (c) 11 (d) 6
3 (a) Nine thousand, three hundred and fifty-four
(b) Twenty-three thousand, nine hundred and eighty-five
(c) Six hundred and seventeen thousand, one hundred and fifty
(d) Three million, five hundred thousand, four hundred and fifty-five
4 (a) 4536 (b) 19 377 (c) 103 567
(d) 5 400 000
5 (a) 35 (b) 24 (c) 72 (d) 42
(e) 36 (f) 40 (g) 54 (h) 63
6 (a) 76 000 (b) 17 900 (c) 90 (d) 88
7 (a) 2 × 18, 3 × 12, 4 × 9, 6 × 6
(b) 2 × 10, 4 × 5

8 (a) 30 000, 200   (b) 6000, 500
    (c) 700 000, 20 000   (d) 70 000, 30
 9 (a) 315   (b) 19   (c) 19   (d) 228
10 (a) 6105   (b) 6594   (c) 47   (d) 17
11 (a) 179   (b) 56
12 (a) 7   (b) 6   (c) 8   (d) 9

Exercise AA

1 Three thousand, four hundred and thirty-nine
2 1794
3 8352
4 16
5 Two of 2 × 36, 3 × 24, 4 × 18, 6 × 12, 8 × 9
6 £156.41
7 £9
8 £653.03
9 513 miles
10 20

18 NUMBER LINES

Exercise 18A

1 A 1; B –9; C –7; D –3; E 3; F –5; G –1
2 S 6; T –10; U –18; V 2; W –2; X –14; Y –6
3 A –13; B –8; C –3; D –11; E 2; F –6; G 4; H –1
4 (a) 3   (b) 6   (c) 3   (d) 3   (e) 6
    (f) 10   (g) 11   (h) 5   (i) 10   (j) 5
    (k) 6   (l) 7

Exercise 18B

1 A 3; B –9; C –5; D –1; E –7; F 1; G –3
2 J –2; K –10; L 2; M –18; N –6; P 6; Q –14
3 A –4; B 4; C 1; D –7; E –11; F –14; G –3; H –9
4 (a) 6   (b) 5   (c) 6   (d) 6   (e) 3
    (f) 3   (g) 1   (h) 11   (i) 4   (j) 12
    (k) 3   (l) 9

Exercise 18C

1 A –5; B –1; C –9; D –7; E –3; F 1; G 3
2 P –6; Q 2; R –18; S –10; T –2; U –14; V 6
3 M –12; N –8; P –1; Q –3; R –11; S –4; T 2; U 4
4 (a) 2   (b) 5   (c) 1   (d) 2   (e) 8
    (f) 6   (g) 4   (h) 11

Exercise 18D

1 A –3; B 1; C –9; D –5; E –1; F –7; G 3
2 M 1; N –4; P –8; Q –6; R –1; S –14; T –11; U 4
3 A 2; B –14; C –1; D –12; E 4; F –6; G –2; H –8
4 (a) 3   (b) 4   (c) 6   (d) 5   (e) 4
    (f) 6   (g) 6   (h) 10

19 ORDERING NUMBERS THAT INCLUDE NEGATIVE NUMBERS

Exercise 19A

1 –2, –1, 1, 2
2 –3, 0, 1, 4
3 3, 1, –1, –2
4 2, 0, –1, –2
5 –4, –3, –2, –1
6 –1, 0, 3, 6
7 1, 0, –1, –2
8 5, 2, 0, –1
9 –5, –4, –3, –2
10 –5, –3, –1, 0
11 –1, –2, –3, –5
12 2, 1, –1, –2
13 –11, –8, –2, 0, 3
14 7, 5, –2, –3, –4
15 3, 1, 0, –1, –2
16 –3, –2, –1, 0, 3
17 4, 1, –1, –2, –3
18 –5, –4, –3, –1, 0
19 5, 2, 1, –1, –3
20 –5, –2, –1, 0, 3
21 2, 1, 0, –1, –2, –3
22 –9, –7, 0, 8, 9, 12
23 24, 23, 11, 0, –1, –2
24 12, 11, 7, –1, –11, –12
25 –21, –19, –3, 0, 3, 5
26 –10, –11, –13, –99, –195, –225
27 625, 346, 335, –56, –87, –124
28 –8, –6, –5, –4, –2, 0, 1
29 –5, –3, –2, –1, 0, 1, 3
30 3, 2, 1, 0, –1, –2, –3

Exercise 19B

1 2, 0, –1, –2
2 5, 4, 0, –1
3 –3, –2, 0, 2
4 –4, –3, –2, –1
5 3, 1, –1, –3
6 3, 2, –1, –2
7 –3, –2, 0, 5
8 –5, –1, 0, 1
9 6, 2, –1, –4
10 1, 0, –2, –3
11 –5, –4, –3, 2
12 –3, –1, 0, 1
13 2, 0, –1, –4, –5
14 –6, –1, 2, 3, 4
15 –7, –6, –2, 9, 10

16 4, 2, 0, –1, –3
17 0, –1, –2, –3, –5
18 –1, 0, 2, 6, 7
19 5, 1, 0, –1, –2
20 0, –1, –2, –3, –4
21 –4, –2, –1, 7, 8, 13
22 –7, –5, –2, –1, 0, 1
23 6, 4, 2, –1, –3, –5
24 –3, –2, –1, 0, 2, 3
25 –14, –13, –12, –10, –9, –8
26 10, 5, –5, –15, –20, –25
27 –95, –99, –127, –136, –137, –140
28 –5, –3, –2, –1, 0, 1, 4
29 –7, –6, –5, –4, –2, 0, 1
30 3, 2, 1, 0, –1, –2, –3

20 NEGATIVE NUMBERS IN CONTEXT

Exercise 20A

1 –2°C	**2** 20 BCE	**3** Fall, 3°C
4 £46	**5** 12.06	**6** 1°C
7 36	**8** 20 m	**9** £22
10 –7°C	**11** 11 cm	**12** Late, 9 min
13 £23	**14** Fall, 5°C	**15** 17 min
16 10 BCE	**17** –5°C	**18** £47
19 6 cm	**20** 12 min	

Exercise 20B

1 5 m	**2** 10 min	**3** 5 cm
4 5°C	**5** £35	**6** Fall, 5°C
7 12.23	**8** –1°C	**9** 21 BCE
10 £23	**11** Fall, 6°C	**12** 4 min 6 s
13 95 BCE	**14** 3°C	**15** £17
16 11 min	**17** Rise, 2°C	**18** £19
19 10 cm	**20** 16 CE	

21 DIRECTED NUMBERS: ADDITION AND SUBTRACTION

Exercise 21A

1 –1	**2** +4	**3** –11	**4** –3
5 –4	**6** +10	**7** –14	**8** –3
9 +16	**10** +2	**11** +7	**12** –18
13 +3	**14** –13	**15** –4	**16** +8
17 0	**18** +1	**19** –12	**20** –12
21 –5	**22** –9	**23** –24	**24** +13
25 +28	**26** –2	**27** +18	**28** –5
29 –3	**30** –16		

Exercise 21B

1 +17	**2** –18	**3** +2	**4** +5
5 –7	**6** –5	**7** +12	**8** +2
9 0	**10** +9	**11** 0	**12** –9
13 +4	**14** +10	**15** –2	**16** +15
17 –14	**18** 0	**19** –2	**20** –2
21 +4	**22** +2	**23** 0	**24** +4
25 –10	**26** 0	**27** +3	**28** –4
29 +7	**30** –8		

Exercise 21C

1 +1	**2** 0	**3** +2	**4** –12
5 +12	**6** –1	**7** +1	**8** +14
9 –1	**10** –4	**11** –16	**12** +3
13 –5	**14** –5	**15** +5	**16** 0
17 –4	**18** –7	**19** –1	**20** –10
21 0	**22** +2	**23** +5	**24** –9
25 +6	**26** –4	**27** –1	**28** –10
29 +9	**30** –1		

Exercise 21D

1 –6	**2** –8	**3** +9	**4** +1
5 –2	**6** –6	**7** –2	**8** +15
9 +2	**10** –7	**11** –1	**12** –9
13 0	**14** –9	**15** +12	**16** –4
17 –4	**18** +2	**19** –17	**20** –3
21 –3	**22** +5	**23** +1	**24** +12
25 –8	**26** –13	**27** +3	**28** +20
29 +1	**30** –6		

22 DIRECTED NUMBERS: MULTIPLICATION AND DIVISION

Exercise 22A

1 +8	**2** –8	**3** +9	**4** –2
5 –12	**6** +3	**7** +5	**8** 0
9 0	**10** –18	**11** +15	**12** +5
13 –9	**14** –30	**15** +8	**16** –24
17 0	**18** –24	**19** –15	**20** –2
21 +8	**22** +30	**23** –10	**24** –18
25 +30	**26** +12	**27** –21	**28** –30
29 +21	**30** –49		

Exercise 22B

1 –15	**2** +15	**3** +8	**4** +30
5 –40	**6** +22	**7** +16	**8** –25
9 +8	**10** –8	**11** +6	**12** +12
13 –16	**14** –6	**15** –12	**16** +5
17 +14	**18** –8	**19** +12	**20** –16
21 0	**22** –28	**23** +12	**24** –3
25 +24	**26** +12	**27** 0	**28** –20
29 +24	**30** –21		

Exercise 22C

1 +2	**2** −3	**3** −3	**4** −1
5 −5	**6** −7	**7** +3	**8** −5
9 −8	**10** +5	**11** −3	**12** −6
13 −3	**14** +4	**15** −4	**16** −5
17 −1	**18** +4	**19** −6	**20** −7
21 +2	**22** −3	**23** −4	**24** −2
25 −2	**26** +2	**27** −4	**28** −4
29 −3	**30** −5		

Exercise 22D

1 +5	**2** −2	**3** −4	**4** +3
5 −4	**6** −6	**7** +6	**8** −5
9 −2	**10** −5	**11** −4	**12** −2
13 +3	**14** −3	**15** +2	**16** −4
17 −2	**18** −2	**19** +3	**20** −4
21 −8	**22** −2	**23** −2	**24** −11
25 +4	**26** −2	**27** −3	**28** +2
29 −5	**30** −3		

23 DIRECTED NUMBERS: MIXED EXAMPLES

Exercise 23A

1 −10	**2** −5	**3** −4	**4** −15
5 −6	**6** +8	**7** +3	**8** −6
9 +6	**10** +12	**11** −5	**12** +9
13 −8	**14** −2	**15** +9	**16** −1
17 −7	**18** −6	**19** +1	**20** +20
21 +4	**22** +13	**23** +4	**24** −6
25 −3	**26** −4	**27** −20	**28** −4
29 −12	**30** −2		

Exercise 23B

1 +6	**2** −3	**3** +18	**4** +6
5 −3	**6** −12	**7** +20	**8** −6
9 +1	**10** +2	**11** +3	**12** −2
13 0	**14** −10	**15** −1	**16** −2
17 +1	**18** −3	**19** −6	**20** +1
21 +3	**22** +1	**23** +9	**24** −3
25 −1	**26** −20	**27** −2	**28** +6
29 +1	**30** −4		

24 RECOGNISING SIMPLE FRACTIONS

Exercise 24A

1 $\frac{2}{3}$	**2** $\frac{3}{5}$	**3** $\frac{3}{8}$	**4** $\frac{5}{6}$
5 $\frac{4}{7}$	**6** $\frac{2}{9}$	**7** $\frac{4}{9}$	**8** $\frac{3}{4}$
9 $\frac{1}{8}$	**10** $\frac{4}{15}$	**11** $\frac{7}{15}$	**12** $\frac{3}{10}$

13 $\frac{7}{10}$	**14** $\frac{5}{24}$	**15** $\frac{7}{24}$	**16** $\frac{1}{12}$
17 $\frac{5}{12}$	**18** $\frac{1}{2}$	**19** $\frac{3}{16}$	**20** $\frac{11}{16}$

Exercise 24B

1 $\frac{4}{5}$	**2** $\frac{7}{8}$	**3** $\frac{3}{4}$	**4** $\frac{1}{9}$
5 $\frac{5}{9}$	**6** $\frac{1}{3}$	**7** $\frac{7}{10}$	**8** $\frac{9}{10}$
9 $\frac{6}{25}$	**10** $\frac{11}{25}$	**11** $\frac{2}{7}$	**12** $\frac{3}{7}$
13 $\frac{1}{12}$	**14** $\frac{7}{12}$	**15** $\frac{1}{4}$	**16** $\frac{9}{20}$
17 $\frac{1}{20}$	**18** $\frac{7}{20}$	**19** $\frac{13}{15}$	**20** $\frac{2}{15}$

25 DRAWING SIMPLE FRACTIONS

Exercise 25A

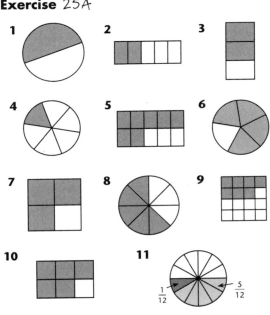

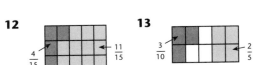

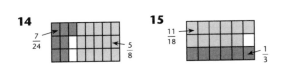

Exercise 25B

1
2
3

4
5
6

7
8
9

10
11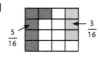

12
13

14
15

26 EQUIVALENT FRACTIONS

Exercise 26A

1 $\frac{3}{4} = \frac{6}{8} = \frac{9}{12} = \frac{24}{32}$

2 $\frac{1}{2} = \frac{2}{4} = \frac{3}{6} = \frac{5}{10}$

3 $\frac{2}{7} = \frac{4}{14} = \frac{6}{21} = \frac{14}{49}$

4 $\frac{1}{16} = \frac{2}{32} = \frac{3}{48} = \frac{5}{80}$

5 $\frac{4}{9} = \frac{8}{18} = \frac{12}{27} = \frac{20}{45}$

6 $\frac{1}{30} = \frac{2}{60} = \frac{3}{90} = \frac{4}{120} = \frac{10}{300}$

7 $\frac{5}{18} = \frac{10}{36} = \frac{20}{72} = \frac{30}{108} = \frac{40}{144}$

8 $\frac{11}{12} = \frac{22}{24} = \frac{33}{48} = \frac{55}{60} = \frac{77}{84}$

9 $\frac{2}{25} = \frac{4}{50} = \frac{8}{100} = \frac{16}{200} = \frac{20}{250}$

10 $\frac{7}{24} = \frac{14}{48} = \frac{21}{72} = \frac{28}{96} = \frac{42}{144}$

Exercise 26B

1 $\frac{2}{3} = \frac{4}{6} = \frac{8}{12} = \frac{12}{18}$

2 $\frac{1}{6} = \frac{2}{12} = \frac{3}{18} = \frac{4}{24}$

3 $\frac{3}{5} = \frac{6}{10} = \frac{12}{20} = \frac{15}{25}$

4 $\frac{2}{15} = \frac{4}{30} = \frac{6}{45} = \frac{12}{90}$

5 $\frac{5}{8} = \frac{10}{16} = \frac{15}{24} = \frac{25}{40}$

6 $\frac{3}{10} = \frac{6}{20} = \frac{9}{30} = \frac{24}{80} = \frac{30}{100}$

7 $\frac{5}{36} = \frac{10}{72} = \frac{15}{108} = \frac{20}{144} = \frac{30}{216}$

8 $\frac{11}{20} = \frac{22}{40} = \frac{33}{60} = \frac{44}{80} = \frac{66}{120}$

9 $\frac{9}{50} = \frac{18}{100} = \frac{27}{150} = \frac{36}{200} = \frac{81}{450}$

10 $\frac{15}{32} = \frac{30}{64} = \frac{45}{96} = \frac{60}{128} = \frac{120}{256}$

27 FRACTIONS OF QUANTITIES

Exercise 27A

1 £7.50	**2** 6 kg	**3** 19 mm
4 4p	**5** £4	**6** 6p
7 £7	**8** 6	**9** 4p
10 4	**11** 24 km	**12** $4
13 75p	**14** 6 mm	**15** 50p
16 6	**17** 16 kg	**18** £1.50
19 2 litres	**20** £3.50	

Exercise 27B

1 4 kg	**2** 12 mm	**3** £3.50
4 8	**5** £3	**6** 28 g
7 5	**8** 2 km	**9** 2 litres
10 £2.50	**11** 5 m	**12** 5 g
13 £0.56	**14** £5	**15** 9 g
16 5 kg	**17** £2	**18** 30p
19 £5	**20** 5p	

Exercise 27C

1 9 cm	**2** 8 km	**3** 35 cm
4 24	**5** £8	**6** 25
7 24 litres	**8** 63 m	**9** £16
10 15	**11** 18 m	**12** 42 litres
13 18 kg	**14** £9	**15** 9
16 32 kg	**17** £3.50	**18** 48 litres
19 15 kg	**20** £21	

Exercise 27D

1 21 m	**2** £15	**3** 18
4 30 g	**5** 30 mm	**6** 33 cm
7 £10	**8** 54 kg	**9** 4 litres

10	12p	11	350	12	£24
13	15 m	14	£40	15	£60
16	180 m	17	6 cm	18	15
19	£18	20	£14		

28 RECOGNISING SIMPLE PERCENTAGES

Exercise 28A

A	25%	B	50%	C	30%	D	6%
E	20%	F	75%	G	60%	H	10%
I	45%	J	5%	K	80%	L	15%
M	35%	N	65%	O	85%	P	2%
Q	8%	R	90%	S	22%	T	78%

Exercise 28B

A	60%	B	30%	C	20%	D	70%
E	75%	F	1%	G	40%	H	50%
I	25%	J	72%	K	5%	L	85%
M	50%	N	15%	O	35%	P	65%
Q	55%	R	45%	S	70%	T	10%

29 DRAWING SIMPLE PERCENTAGES

Exercise 29A

1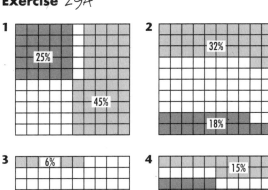

2

3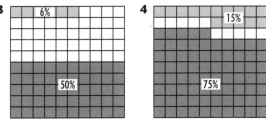

4

5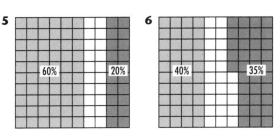

6

7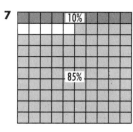

8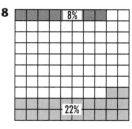

9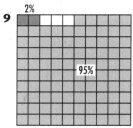

10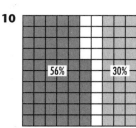

11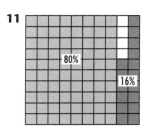

12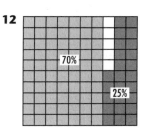

13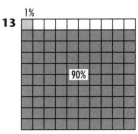

14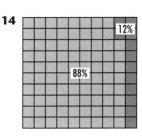

15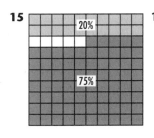

16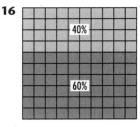

17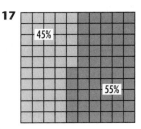

18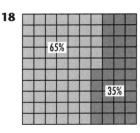

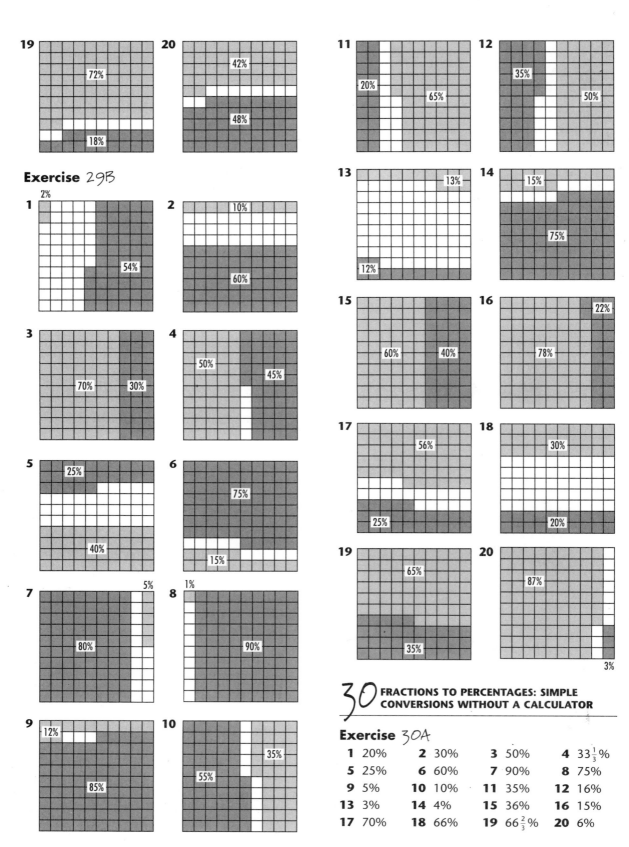

19 72% 18%

20 42% 48%

11 20% 65%

12 35% 50%

Exercise 29B

1 2% 54%

2 10% 60%

13 13% 12%

14 15% 75%

3 70% 30%

4 50% 45%

15 60% 40%

16 78% 22%

5 25% 40%

6 75% 15%

17 56% 25%

18 30% 20%

7 5% 80%

8 1% 90%

19 65% 35%

20 87% 3%

9 12% 85%

10 55% 35%

30 FRACTIONS TO PERCENTAGES: SIMPLE CONVERSIONS WITHOUT A CALCULATOR

Exercise 30A

1 20%	**2** 30%	**3** 50%	**4** $33\frac{1}{3}$%
5 25%	**6** 60%	**7** 90%	**8** 75%
9 5%	**10** 10%	**11** 35%	**12** 16%
13 3%	**14** 4%	**15** 36%	**16** 15%
17 70%	**18** 66%	**19** $66\frac{2}{3}$%	**20** 6%

Exercise 30B

1 75%	**2** 50%	**3** 40%	**4** 5%
5 $66\frac{2}{3}$%	**6** 75%	**7** 8%	**8** 25%
9 20%	**10** $33\frac{1}{3}$%	**11** 80%	**12** 21%
13 14%	**14** 55%	**15** 85%	**16** 60%
17 12%	**18** 1%	**19** 47%	**20** 35%

31 FRACTIONS TO PERCENTAGES WITH A CALCULATOR

Exercise 31A

1 40	**2** 37.5	**3** 33.333*
4 18	**5** 85	**6** 20
7 65	**8** 22.5	**9** 12.5
10 16	**11** 22.222*	**12** 24
13 11.111*	**14** 36	**15** 87.5
16 16.667*	**17** 47.5	**18** 58
19 44	**20** 41.667*	

Exercise 31B

1 28	**2** 15	**3** 80
4 66.667*	**5** 42	**6** 75
7 4	**8** 60	**9** 32
10 44.444*	**11** 62.5	**12** 84
13 95	**14** 83.333*	**15** 72
16 74	**17** 58.333*	**18** 12
19 72.5	**20** 96	

*Accept alternative versions and condone errors that are not relevant to the process tested.

32 PERCENTAGES TO FRACTIONS: SIMPLE CONVERSIONS WITHOUT A CALCULATOR

Exercise 32A

1 $\frac{1}{2}$	**2** $\frac{1}{4}$	**3** $\frac{1}{100}$	**4** $\frac{1}{20}$
5 $\frac{9}{20}$	**6** $\frac{1}{10}$	**7** $\frac{9}{10}$	**8** $\frac{7}{100}$
9 $\frac{2}{5}$	**10** $\frac{19}{100}$	**11** $\frac{13}{20}$	**12** $\frac{3}{25}$
13 $\frac{1}{3}$	**14** $\frac{11}{50}$	**15** $\frac{1}{25}$	**16** 1
17 $\frac{3}{50}$	**18** $\frac{3}{10}$	**19** $\frac{17}{50}$	**20** $\frac{4}{25}$

Exercise 32B

1 $\frac{3}{100}$	**2** $\frac{3}{4}$	**3** $\frac{1}{50}$	**4** $\frac{3}{20}$
5 $\frac{7}{10}$	**6** $\frac{7}{20}$	**7** $\frac{13}{100}$	**8** $\frac{2}{25}$
9 $\frac{3}{5}$	**10** $\frac{21}{100}$	**11** $\frac{2}{3}$	**12** $\frac{13}{50}$
13 $\frac{17}{20}$	**14** $\frac{17}{100}$	**15** $\frac{19}{20}$	**16** $\frac{4}{5}$

17 $\frac{11}{25}$	**18** $\frac{1}{5}$	**19** $\frac{6}{25}$	**20** $\frac{11}{20}$

33 CALCULATING PERCENTAGES OF QUANTITIES WITHOUT A CALCULATOR

Exercise 33A

1 5 m	**2** £6	**3** 18 cm	**4** £10
5 6p	**6** 44p	**7** 6 km	**8** 2
9 35p	**10** 42p	**11** 10 g	**12** 10p
13 £1.30	**14** 16 mm	**15** 30	**16** 36p
17 4 ml	**18** 24p	**19** 60p	**20** £12

Exercise 33B

1 7p	**2** 8 kg	**3** 18p	**4** 6
5 15 km	**6** 14p	**7** £20	**8** 55p
9 20	**10** 32p	**11** £1	**12** 4
13 12 g	**14** 18p	**15** 12	**16** £6
17 30p	**18** 12	**19** 34p	**20** 15

34 CALCULATING PERCENTAGES OF QUANTITIES WITH A CALCULATOR

Exercise 34A

1 £4.14	**2** 27	**3** 67.2 kg
4 £8.40	**5** £3.25	**6** 1.36 m
7 63	**8** £6	**9** 24 ml
10 £5.13	**11** 7.84 m	**12** 1.65 km
13 1.96 kg	**14** £18.15	**15** 2.72
16 3 g	**17** £4.16	**18** 73.5
19 27.2 km	**20** 151.8	

Exercise 34B

1 £3.15	**2** £1.89	**3** 3.14
4 £0.87	**5** 1.912 km	**6** 7.56 m
7 £8.40	**8** 59.4 km	**9** 20.25
10 £84.50	**11** 36.8 kg	**12** 2.7 g
13 £14.07	**14** 22.5	**15** 126 m
16 42 kg	**17** £17.03	**18** 43.2
19 £4.83	**20** £86.8	

35 PROBLEMS INVOLVING SIMPLE PERCENTAGES OF QUANTITIES

Exercise 35A

1 12	**2** 19	**3** 14p
4 300 ml	**5** £11.25	**6** 36
7 £7.40	**8** 35	**9** 153 g
10 £1.56	**11** £288	**12** 200 g
13 14 km	**14** 150 ml	**15** £54
16 £108		

Exercise 35B

1 24	**2** 108	**3** 110 ml
4. £4.70	**5** 52 mm	**6** £13.80
7 8.4 litres	**8** £19.95	**9** 16.8 g
10 10.8 g	**11** 900	**12** £90.72
13 67 500	**14** 60 g	**15** £45.60
16 £280		

36 IDENTIFYING TYPES OF NUMBER

Exercise 36A

1 18
2 13
3 5, 15, 25
4 1, 36, 64
5 None

6 (a) 8, 12	(b) 14, 35	(c) 4, 36	(d) 19, 31
7 (a) 15, 45	(b) 8, 32	(c) 11, 23	(d) 9, 49
8 (a) 10, 20	(b) 12, 27	(c) 1, 64	(d) 13, 29
9 (a) 16, 81	(b) 12, 18	(c) 7, 37	(d) 10, 20
10 (a) 14, 21	(b) 25, 121	(c) 8, 24	(d) 5, 17
11 (a) 8	(b) 29	(c) 21	(d) 5
(e) 18	(f) 16		
12 (a) 10	(b) 21	(c) 14	(d) 13
(e) 15	(f) 25		

Exercise 36B

1 15
2 8
3 29, 31, 37
4 9, 16, 25
5 6, 8, 12, 16, 24

6 (a) 6, 18	(b) 8, 24	(c) 49, 169	(d) 13, 53
7 (a) 25, 64	(b) 15, 21	(c) 19, 23	(d) 4, 8
8 (a) 4, 8	(b) 20, 50	(c) 36, 81	(d) 29, 31
9 (a) 21, 28	(b) 12, 20	(c) 36, 100	(d) 17, 23
10 (a) 6, 8	(b) 16, 49	(c) 18, 27	(d) 29, 61
11 (a) 30	(b) 31	(c) 39	(d) 25
(e) 18	(f) 100		
12 (a) 3	(b) 18	(c) 6	(d) 5
(e) 20	(f) 81		

R EVISION

Exercise B

1 −7, −5, −1, 0, 5

2 (a) −6	(b) −9	(c) +2	(d) −1

3

4

5 $\frac{7}{16}$, $\frac{9}{16}$

6 $\frac{1}{6}$, $\frac{5}{6}$

7 $\frac{2}{3}$ = $\frac{4}{6}$ = $\frac{6}{9}$ = $\frac{14}{21}$

8 A 35%; B 25%; unshaded 40%

9

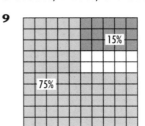

10%

10 (a) 75%	(b) 50%	(c) 40%	(d) 30%
11 (a) $\frac{1}{4}$	(b) $\frac{3}{5}$	(c) $\frac{1}{20}$	(d) $\frac{1}{5}$
12 (a) 9 kg	(b) £9	(c) 400	(d) £7.50
13 (a) 15p	(b) 10	(c) 40	(d) 30
14 (a) 24, 60	(b) 8, 20	(c) 29, 53	(d) 25, 64

Exercise BB

1 15 CE
2 Fallen 9°C
3 27 min
4 £25
5 20
6 £36
7 £2.40
8 $\frac{5}{8}$, £9
9 £45, 40%
10 66 g
11 4.8 g
12 £109.20

13 (a) 32	(b) 14	(c) 15	(d) 7
(e) 9	(f) 36		

Algebra

37 SIMPLE EQUATIONS

Exercise 37A

1 4	**2** 7	**3** 6	**4** 15	**5** 7
6 5	**7** 3	**8** 3	**9** 4	**10** 9
11 7	**12** 30	**13** 6	**14** 4	**15** 12
16 7	**17** 18	**18** 0	**19** 10	**20** 8
21 3	**22** 3	**23** 8	**24** 5	**25** 9
26 5	**27** 2	**28** 8	**29** 7	**30** 4

Exercise 37B

1 17	**2** 3	**3** 6	**4** 8	**5** 9
6 5	**7** 6	**8** 28	**9** 5	**10** 8
11 5	**12** 3	**13** 6	**14** 13	**15** 2
16 20	**17** 9	**18** 42	**19** 17	**20** 3
21 45	**22** 4	**23** 2	**24** 2	**25** 6
26 12	**27** 16	**28** 11	**29** 4	**30** 7

38 ALGEBRAIC EQUATIONS

Exercise 38A

1 2	**2** 3	**3** 5	**4** 3	**5** 8
6 1	**7** 4	**8** 25	**9** 4	**10** 11
11 9	**12** 3	**13** 1	**14** 6	**15** 4
16 2	**17** 12	**18** 13	**19** 8	**20** 2
21 7	**22** 2	**23** 5	**24** 1	**25** 9
26 4	**27** 2	**28** 5	**29** 4	**30** 7

Exercise 38B

1 4	**2** 7	**3** 3	**4** 4	**5** 12
6 7	**7** 5	**8** 3	**9** 12	**10** 7
11 4	**12** 5	**13** 8	**14** 8	**15** 4
16 1	**17** 7	**18** 3	**19** 12	**20** 6
21 3	**22** 7	**23** 9	**24** 2	**25** 2
26 0	**27** 3	**28** 2	**29** 5	**30** 3

39 CONTINUING A NUMBER SEQUENCE

Exercise 39A

1 13, 15	**2** 15, 13	**3** 50, 60
4 19, 22	**5** 25, 30	**6** 15, 16
7 27, 30	**8** 25, 36	**9** 55, 77

10 20, 24	**11** 20, 18	**12** 32, 37
13 25, 19	**14** 22, 21	**15** −10, −12
16 31, 27	**17** 30, 36	**18** 35, 30
19 72, 79	**20** 42, 49	**21** 4, 8
22 11, 16	**23** 13, 12	**24** 5, 2.5
25 57, 53	**26** 26, 37	**27** 10, 12
28 15, 17	**29** −10, −13	**30** 29, 22

Exercise 39B

1 20, 22	**2** 52, 49	**3** 50, 60
4 10, 11	**5** 90, 88	**6** 20, 24
7 33, 39	**8** 35, 43	**9** 32, 64
10 30, 33	**11** 20, 19	**12** 28, 39
13 9, 11	**14** −4, −5	**15** 16, 8
16 26, 31	**17** 60, 53	**18** 25, 30
19 $\frac{1}{2}, \frac{1}{4}$	**20** 31, 27	**21** 25, 36
22 32, 24	**23** 13, $14\frac{1}{2}$	**24** 63, 54
25 42, 50	**26** 24, 31	**27** 11, 15
28 50, 60	**29** 53, 51	**30** 32, 24

40 PREDICTING THE TERMS IN A SEQUENCE

Exercise 40A

1 Add 3; 50, 53
2 Add 1; 13, 14
3 Multiples of 5; 25, 35
4 Add 3; 26, 29
5 Subtract 2; 27, 21
6 Multiples of 6; 30, 42
7 Subtract 2; 38, 34
8 Multiples of 5 greater than 15; 45, 50
9 Add 2; 21, 25
10 Multiples of 3; 21, 24
11 Subtract 4; 21, 17
12 Add 7; 52, 66
13 Double; 64, 128
14 Multiples of 4; 24, 36
15 Even numbers; 16, 20
16 Subtract 8; 29, 13
17 Add 1; 15, 16
18 Subtract 5; 23, 18
19 Subtract 2; 11, 9
20 Multiples of 10; 90, 100

Exercise 40B

1 Add 4; 28, 32
2 Multiples of 3 greater than 9; 24, 27
3 Difference is increasing by 6; 80, 113
4 Multiples of 2; 10, 16
5 Add 6; 43, 49
6 Multiples of 4; 24, 36
7 Add 2; 45, 49
8 Subtract 1; 9, 5
9 Multiples of 10; 60, 90
10 Add 1; 26, 29
11 Odd numbers greater than 10; 27, 29
12 Difference is increasing by −1; 16, 7
13 Subtract 2; 49, 45
14 Subtract 1; 12, 11
15 Difference is increasing by 1; 40, 49
16 Double or powers of 2; 32, 128
17 Add 3; 32, 38
18 Add 8; 60, 68
19 Add 2; 41, 45
20 Multiples of 6; 42, 60

41 COLLECTING LIKE TERMS

Exercise 41A

1 $2a$	2 $3b$	3 $4d$
4 $3e$	5 $3b$	6 $5c$
7 $2e$	8 $2a$	9 c
10 $5d$	11 $6a$	12 $7b$
13 $6d$	14 $9e$	15 $4b$
16 $5a + 6b$	17 $3a + 4b$	18 $5a + 3b - 4c$
19 $a + b$	20 $4a + 6b$	

Exercise 41B

1 $3v$	2 $2w$	3 $2y$
4 $3z$	5 $4w$	6 x
7 $9z$	8 $4v$	9 $4x$
10 $6y$	11 v	12 $6w$
13 $9y$	14 $7z$	15 $w + 7v$
16 $4x - 5y$	17 $7x + y$	18 $3x - 2y$
19 $5x + 3y$	20 $w + v$	

Exercise 41C

1 $a + a$
2 $b + b$
3 $d + d + d$
4 $e + e$
5 $b + b + b + b + b$
6 $c + c$
7 $e + e + e + e + e$
8 $a + a + b + b$
9 $c + c + c + d + d$
10 $d + d + d + e$
11 $a + a - b - b$
12 $b + b + b - c$
13 $d + d + e + e + e$
14 $e + e - f - f - f$
15 $b + b + b + c + c$
16 $c + c - d - d - d$
17 $e + e + e + f + f - g$
18 $a + b + b + c + c$
19 $c - d - d - d + e + e$
20 $d + d + e + e + f + f$

Exercise 41D

1 $v + v + v$
2 $w + w$
3 $y + y + y + y$
4 $z + z + z$
5 $w + w + w + w$
6 $x + x + x$
7 $z + z + z + z + z + z$
8 $v + v + w + w$
9 $x + x + y + y + y$
10 $y + y + y - z$
11 $w + w - v - v - v$
12 $w + w + x + x - z$
13 $x + x + x + x + x - y - y - y$
14 $v + v - w - w$
15 $w + x + x + x + x$
16 $x + x + x + y - z$
17 $y + y - x - x - x - z$
18 $a + a + a - b - b + c$
19 $x + x + x - y - y - y$
20 $x + x - y - z$

42 FUNCTION MACHINES: FINDING OUTPUTS

Exercise 42A

	(a)	(b)	(c)	(d)
1	3	7	11	15
2	25	19	13	7
3	4	8	12	16
4	6	7	8	9
5	8	15	22	29
6	29	32	35	38
7	18	34	50	66
8	43	31	19	7
9	5	6	7	10
10	11	10	9	8

Exercise 42B

1 (a) 9	(b) 17	(c) 25	(d) 33
2 (a) 1	(b) 5	(c) 9	(d) 13
3 (a) 6	(b) 9	(c) 11	(d) 13
4 (a) 140	(b) 110	(c) 50	(d) 20
5 (a) 4	(b) 22	(c) 40	(d) 220
6 (a) 25	(b) 29	(c) 33	(d) 85
7 (a) 2	(b) 3	(c) 4	(d) 22
8 (a) 8	(b) 14	(c) 20	(d) 152
9 (a) 11	(b) 19	(c) 35	(d) 131
10 (a) 24	(b) 8	(c) 0	(d) –7

43 FUNCTION MACHINES: FINDING INPUTS

Exercise 43A

1 (a) 3	(b) 4	(c) 5	(d) 6
2 (a) 12	(b) 10	(c) 8	(d) 6
3 (a) 6	(b) 5	(c) 4	(d) 3
4 (a) 0	(b) 3	(c) 6	(d) 9
5 (a) 3	(b) 4	(c) 5	(d) 6
6 (a) 21	(b) 24	(c) 27	(d) 72
7 (a) 4	(b) 5	(c) 6	(d) 25
8 (a) 0	(b) 4	(c) 8	(d) 12
9 (a) 5	(b) 6	(c) 7	(d) 11
10 (a) 2	(b) 4	(c) 6	(d) 32

Exercise 43B

1 (a) 4	(b) 6	(c) 8	(d) 10
2 (a) 5	(b) 6	(c) 7	(d) 8
3 (a) 33	(b) 36	(c) 39	(d) 42
4 (a) 16	(b) 15	(c) 14	(d) 13
5 (a) 0	(b) 5	(c) 10	(d) 90
6 (a) 2	(b) 4	(c) 6	(d) 20
7 (a) 12	(b) 16	(c) 20	(d) 212
8 (a) 36	(b) 30	(c) 24	(d) 600
9 (a) 2	(b) 4	(c) 6	(d) 12
10 (a) 12	(b) 16	(c) 20	(d) 40

44 FUNCTION MACHINES: FINDING INPUTS AND OUTPUTS

Exercise 44A

1 3, 5, 7, 9	**2** 1, 4, 7, 10
3 5, 6, 7, 8	**4** 12, 14, 16, 18
5 2, 4, 6, 8	**6** 1, 2, 3, 4
7 2, 3, 4, 5	**8** 15, 18, 21, 24
9 13, 15, 17, 19	**10** 0, 1, 2, 3
11 3, 4, 5, 6	**12** 8, 12, 16, 20
13 5, 11, 17, 23	**14** 5, 7, 9, 11
15 4, 8, 12, 16	**16** 6, 7, 8, 9
17 9, 14, 19, 24	**18** 2, 3, 4, 5
19 16, 23, 30, 37	**20** 25, 30, 35, 40

Exercise 44B

1 1, 3, 5, 7	**2** 4, 7, 10, 13
3 2 ,3 ,4, 5	**4** 12, 16, 20, 24
5 1, 2, 3, 4	**6** 3, 4, 5, 6
7 0, 3, 6, 9	**8** 22, 26, 30, 34
9 8, 12, 16, 20	**10** 2, 3, 4, 5
11 1, 2, 3, 4	**12** 8, 13, 18, 23
13 9, 12, 15, 18	**14** 0, 1, 2, 3
15 –1, 1, 3, 5	**16** 7, 11, 15, 19
17 4, 5, 6, 7	**18** 7, 11, 15, 19
19 18, 21, 24, 27	**20** 2, 7, 12, 17

45 FUNCTION MACHINES: FINDING THE FUNCTION

Exercise 45A

1 $+2$	**2** -1	**3** $\times 2$	**4** -5
5 $+4$	**6** $\times 2$	**7** $+10$	**8** -4
9 $\times 7$	**10** $\div 2$	**11** -3	**12** $\times 3$
13 -2	**14** $\div 4$	**15** $\times 6$	**16** $\div 5$
17 $\div 3$	**18** $\times 10$	**19** -8	**20** $\times 5$

Exercise 45B

1 -4	**2** $+3$	**3** $\div 2$	**4** $+4$
5 $\times 2$	**6** $\div 10$	**7** $+2$	**8** $\times 5$
9 $+1$	**10** -3	**11** -10	**12** $\div 6$
13 $\times 3$	**14** $+5$	**15** $\div 4$	**16** $\times 7$
17 $\times 2$	**18** $\div 2$	**19** $\div 5$	**20** $\times 10$

Exercise 45C

1 $\div 2$	**2** $\times 2, +2$	**3** $+5$
4 -7	**5** $+1$	**6** $\times 3$
7 $\times 5$	**8** $\times 2, +1$	**9** $\times 2, +2$
10 $\div 2, +1$	**11** $\div 2$	**12** $\times 2, +1$
13 $\div 2$	**14** $\times 2, +1$	**15** $\times 2, +3$
16 $+2$	**17** -9	**18** $+3, \div 2$
19 $\times 2, -1$	**20** $\times 2, +3$	

Exercise 45D

1 $\times 2$	**2** $\div 2$	**3** $\times 3$
4 $\times 2$	**5** $\div 3$	**6** $\times 5$
7 $+4$	**8** $\div 3$	**9** $\times 2, -2$
10 $\div 5$	**11** $\times 6$	**12** $\times 2, -1$
13 -2	**14** $\times 2, +1$	**15** $\div 5$
16 $+5$	**17** $\times 2, +2$	**18** -1
19 $\times 2, +1$	**20** $\times 2$	

Exercise C

1 (a) 4   (b) 6   (c) 9   (d) 4
    (e) 5   (f) 9   (g) 13   (h) 7

2 (a) 12   (b) 4   (c) 3   (d) 6
    (e) 8   (f) 2   (g) 6   (h) 6

3 (a) 13, 15   (b) 12, 1   (c) 12, 17   (d) 15, 18

4 (a) 25, 30; + 5
    (b) 11, 16; difference increases by 1
    (c) 66, 60; difference increases by −1
    (d) 16, 32; × 2

5 (a) $2g$ (b) $5h$ (c) i (d) $5j + 2k$

6 (a) $p + p + p$ (b) $q + q + q + q + q$
    (c) $r + r + r - s - s$ (d) $t + t + u + u - w$

7 (a) 7   (b) 13   (c) 19   (d) 31

8 (a) 1   (b) 5   (c) 9   (d) 13

9 (a) 3   (b) 4   (c) 5   (d) 7

10 (a) 6   (b) 8   (c) 10   (d) 14

11 (a) + 4   (b) × 2   (c) − 1   (d) × 3

Exercise CC

1 (a) (i) Add 2   (ii) 29, 33
    (b) (i) Subtract 3   (ii) 20, 17
    (c) (i) × 2   (ii) 16, 32
    (d) (i) Add 10   (ii) 5, 65

2 (a) 14, 18, 22, 24   (b) 4, 19, 49, 70

3 (a) 0, 1, 2, 3   (b) 7, 8, 9, 11
    (c) 7, 12, 17, 22   (d) 3, 9, 15, 27

4 1, 12 terms

5 4, 9; 5, 14; 7, 27; 11, 65; 101

46 MULTIPLICATION AND DIVISION IN ALGEBRA

Exercise $46A$

1 $a \times b$ **2** $b \times c$

3 $3 \times d$ **4** $2 \times d \times e$

5 $5 \times b \times c$ **6** $b \times b$

7 $3 \times a \times a$ **8** $a \div b$

9 $c \div d$ **10** $2 \times a \div b$

11 $a \times a \div b$ **12** $5 \times c \div 3$

13 $c \times c \div d$ **14** $4 \times a \div c$

15 $d \div e$ **16** $e \times e$

17 a **18** $5 \times b \div 2$

19 $a \times b \times c$ **20** $2 \times a \times b \times c$

Exercise $46B$

1 $p \times q$ **2** $q \times r$

3 $5 \times t$ **4** $3 \times p \times q$

5 $p \times p$ **6** $q \times q$

7 $3 \times r \times r$ **8** $p \div q$

9 $2 \times r \div s$ **10** $3 \times q \div 5$

11 $r \times r \div p$ **12** $2 \times r \div 3$

13 $s \times s \div 3$ **14** $3 \times q$

15 $t \times t \div 2$ **16** $2 \times t \times t$

17 $2 \times p \times q \times r$ **18** $p \times p \div q$

19 $s \times t \times u$ **20** $s \times s \times t$

Exercise $46C$

1 $\dfrac{a}{b}$ **2** ab **3** a^2 **4** bc

5 $\dfrac{a}{2}$ **6** $\dfrac{2}{a}$ **7** $\dfrac{d}{5}$ **8** $5d$

9 $2ab$ **10** $3e^2$ **11** $\dfrac{7b}{c}$ **12** $\dfrac{ab}{2}$

13 $\dfrac{6}{b}$ **14** $\dfrac{c}{7}$ **15** $\dfrac{ab}{c}$ **16** $\dfrac{3de}{5}$

17 $6bc$ **18** $3bcd$ **19** $\dfrac{3c}{4}$ **20** b^2c

Exercise $46D$

1 pr **2** qs **3** $2p$ **4** $2p^2$

5 $\dfrac{3}{q}$ **6** $\dfrac{r}{4}$ **7** $\dfrac{t}{u}$ **8** st

9 $3st$ **10** $5s^2$ **11** $\dfrac{pq}{3}$ **12** $\dfrac{s^2}{t}$

13 $\dfrac{qr}{2}$ **14** $\dfrac{s^2}{p}$ **15** $\dfrac{pqr}{4}$ **16** $\dfrac{1}{p}$

17 $2p^2$ **18** $2p^2q$ **19** $\dfrac{10s}{t}$ **20** $3stu$

47 MULTIPLYING OUT BRACKETS

Exercise $47A$

1 $2a + 6$ **2** $3x - 12$ **3** $20 - 4b$

4 $2c + 12$ **5** $5x + 10$ **6** $6 - 3a$

7 $2x + 8$ **8** $5a - 15$ **9** $18 + 3b$

10 $2a + 2b$ **11** $3x - 3y$ **12** $5a + 5b$

13 $2x + 2y$ **14** $4a - 4b$ **15** $3a + 3b$

16 $7x - 7y$ **17** $2a - 2b$ **18** $4x + 4y$

19 $5x - 15$ **20** $3a + 12$ **21** $6 + 4a$

22 $6a - 9$ **23** $10x - 5$ **24** $4a + 6$

25 $4 - 12b$ **26** $10 + 4c$ **27** $4a - 2b$

28 $6x + 15y$ **29** $20b - 10$ **30** $6a - 9b$

Exercise $47B$

1 $2s - 6$ **2** $5p + 10$ **3** $12 - 3q$

4 $25 - 5p$ **5** $2r + 6$ **6** $4s + 4$

7 $2s + 12$ **8** $3p - 12$ **9** $6 + 2q$

10 $2s - 2t$ **11** $3p + 3q$ **12** $4p + 4q$

13 $5s + 5t$ **14** $3p + 3q$ **15** $2p - 2q$

16 $7s - 7t$ **17** $6p - 6q$ **18** $3s + 3t$

19 $4s - 12$ 20 $3p + 9$ 21 $6 + 9p$
22 $4p - 2$ 23 $10s - 15$ 24 $9p + 12$
25 $5 - 10q$ 26 $10 + 4r$ 27 $6p - 9q$
28 $12s + 20t$ 29 $10q - 16$ 30 $9p - 12q$

22 9 cm   23 17   24 20
25 16   26 7   27 6
28 6   29 800 g   30 30 g

48 SUBSTITUTION INTO ALGEBRAIC EXPRESSIONS

Exercise 48A

1 10	2 20	3 6	4 7
5 1	6 10	7 8	8 20
9 2	10 2	11 3	12 20
13 60	14 40	15 25	16 1
17 9	18 32	19 64	20 17
21 0	22 13	23 14	24 29
25 19	26 10	27 4	28 21
29 5	30 16		

Exercise 48B

1 3	2 16	3 16	4 12
5 4	6 32	7 4	8 2
9 4	10 $1\frac{1}{2}$	11 3	12 10
13 16	14 12	15 64	16 100
17 1	18 36	19 18	20 29
21 4	22 19	23 18	24 15
25 7	26 26	27 21	28 6
29 16	30 25		

49 EQUATIONS AND FORMULAE IN WORDS

Exercise 49A

1 9	2 50 cm	3 12
4 6 cm	5 14°	6 180 min
7 28	8 7 years	9 7
10 60°	11 6	12 4 cm
13 9	14 268 miles	15 40 min
16 13	17 3 hours	18 10
19 10	20 10	21 20 years
22 7	23 £11	24 100 cm
25 42°	26 8	27 60 ml
28 15	29 13°	30 £12

Exercise 49B

1 16	2 15 years	3 13
4 3 cm	5 17	6 10
7 6 km	8 11	9 £75
10 65°	11 6	12 3 days
13 14	14 58 kg	15 6
16 9	17 18	18 7
19 4	20 16	21 26 cm

50 WRITING ALGEBRAIC EXPRESSIONS

Exercise 50A

1 $7 + b$	2 $c - 6$	3 $3d$
4 $\frac{f}{5}$	5 $e + 5$	6 $8 - e$
7 $\frac{1}{b}$	8 gh	9 $h + g$
10 pq	11 $\frac{10}{c}$	12 $b - 3$
13 $d + 12$	14 xy	15 $\frac{d}{3}$
16 $10d$ cm	17 $(h - n)$ hours	18 $g + b$
19 £$3h$	20 $\frac{A}{8}$ cm^2	21 $6c$ cm
22 $(h + p)$ m^2	23 $52 - n$	24 $7w$
25 $b + 2c$	26 £$(a + b)$	27 $n + 2$
28 $\frac{1}{n}$	29 $3x$	30 $m + 1$

Exercise 50B

1 $20 + c$	2 $a - 10$	3 $\frac{8}{a}$
4 $9f$	5 $\frac{r}{s}$	6 $q + p$
7 $h - g$	8 $r + s$	9 $7c$
10 $\frac{e}{4}$	11 st	12 $f + 6$
13 $6e$	14 $s - t$	15 $\frac{t}{u}$
16 $(m + n)$ min	17 $(180 - m)$ min	18 $1000k$ km
19 $\frac{£P}{32}$	20 £$(S - n)$	21 $(a + b)$ cm
22 $10c$ g	23 $54q$ s	24 $(k + p)$ kg
25 $(A - B)$ cm^2	26 nx g	27 $\frac{y}{60}$ min
28 $2(a + b)$	29 $\frac{£J}{4}$	30 $n - 1$

51 SUBSTITUTING INTO SIMPLE FORMULAE

Exercise 51A

1 (a) 60	(b) 78.4	2 (a) 20	(b) 32	
3 (a) 20	(b) 17	4 (a) 60	(b) 32	
5 (a) 9	(b) 3.5	6 (a) 25	(b) 2.25	

7	(a) 5	(b) 4.54	8	(a) 18	(b) 20
9	(a) 3	(b) 4.5	10	(a) 5	(b) $\frac{1}{5}$
11	(a) 36	(b) 12	12	(a) 48	(b) 300
13	(a) 450	(b) 784	14	(a) 5	(b) 4.2
15	(a) 120	(b) 62	16	(a) 80	(b) 250
17	(a) 9	(b) 2	18	(a) 60	(b) 150
19	(a) 20	(b) 35	20	(a) 12	(b) 10

Exercise 51B

1	(a) 240	(b) 150	2	(a) 64	(b) 0.5
3	(a) 500	(b) 360	4	(a) 30	(b) 18.6
5	(a) 12	(b) 36	6	(a) 25	(b) 53
7	(a) 56	(b) 1900	8	(a) 80	(b) 260
9	(a) 20	(b) 40	10	(a) 5	(b) 7
11	(a) 4	(b) 40	12	(a) 50	(b) 68
13	(a) 13	(b) 5	14	(a) 225	(b) 40
15	(a) 20	(b) 360	16	(a) 25	(b) 20
17	(a) 80	(b) 0.2	18	(a) 30	(b) 24
19	(a) 10	(b) 500	20	(a) 36	(b) 60

52 NAMING POINTS IN THE FIRST QUADRANT

Exercise 52A

1 A(1, 2), B(2, 3), C(3, 4), D(4, 5), E(1, 4), F(3, 2)

2 G(1, 1), H(1, 2), I(1, 3), J(1, 4), K(2, 4), L(3, 4), M(4, 4), N(4, 1)

3 P(1, 0), Q(0, 1), R(2, 0), S(0, 2), T(3, 0), U(0, 3), V(3, 1), W(1, 3)

4 A(2, 4), B(2, 3), C(3, 4), D(3, 3), E(4, 4), F(4, 3), G(5, 4), H(5, 3)

5 I(1, 1), J(2, 2), K(3, 3), L(4, 4), M(2, 1), N(3, 2), P(4, 3), Q(5, 4)

6 R(1, 4), S(2, 3), T(3, 2), U(4, 1), V(0, 3), W(1, 2), X(2, 1), Y(3, 0)

Exercise 52B

1 A(2, 4), B(3, 4), C(4, 4), D(4, 3), E(4, 2), F(3, 2), G(2, 2), H(2, 3), I(3, 3)

2 J(1, 5), K(2, 4), L(3, 3), M(4, 2), N(5, 1), P(0, 0), Q(1, 1), R(2, 2)

3 S(5, 5), T(5, 1), U(4, 0), V(2, 0), W(0, 5), X(0, 2), Y(3, 5)

4 A(0, 3), B(1, 4), C(2, 5), D(3, 5), E(4, 4), F(5, 3), G(2, 2), H(3, 2)

5 I(2, 4), J(3, 3), K(4, 4), L(4, 2), M(5, 1), N(3, 1), P(2, 2), Q(1, 3)

6 R(1, 4), S(2, 4), T(3, 4), U(4, 4), V(1, 2), W(2, 2), X(3, 2), Y(4, 2)

53 PLOTTING POINTS IN THE FIRST QUADRANT

Exercise 53A

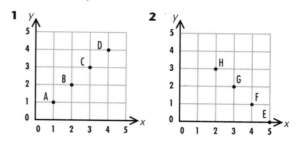

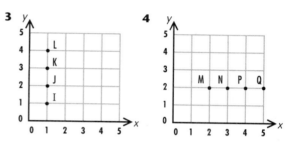

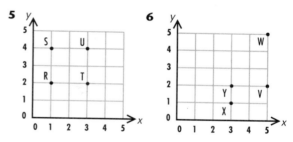

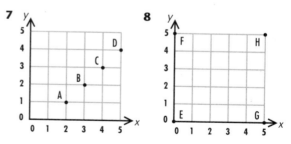

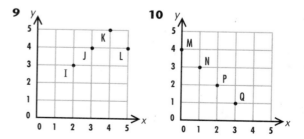

Exercise 53B

1
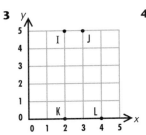

2
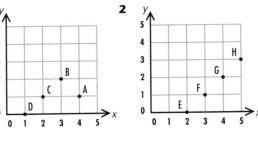

3

4
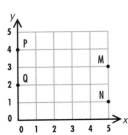

5
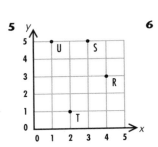

6
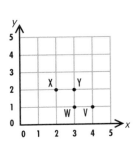

7
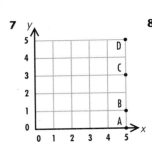

8
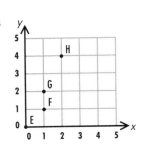

9
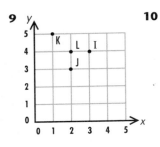

10
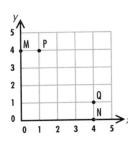

Exercise 53C

1
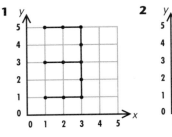

2
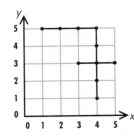

3
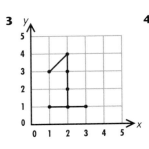

4
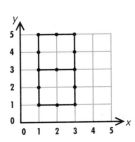

5
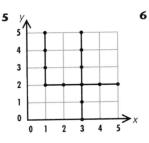

6
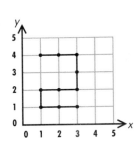

7
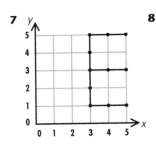

8
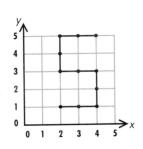

Exercise 53D

1
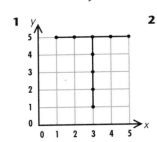

2
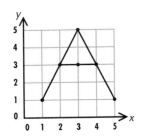

ALGEBRA **21**

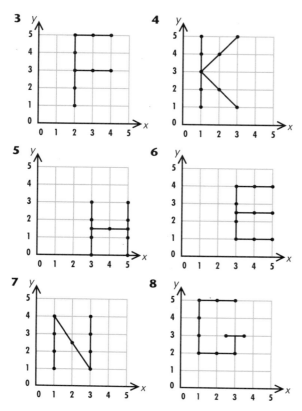

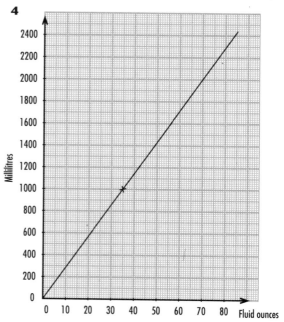

(a) 1800 ml, 800 ml, 200 ml, 1600 ml
(b) 49 fl. oz, 70 fl. oz, 42 fl. oz, 14 fl. oz

54 DRAWING AND INTERPRETING CONVERSION GRAPHS

Exercise 54A

1 (a) 1100–1150 ml, 2800 ml, 3650 ml, 3200 ml
   (b) 6.2 pints, 4.0 pints, 3.0 pints, 9.1 pints
2 (a) 21 francs, 45 francs, 15 francs, 29 francs
   (b) $6.80, $5.10, $7.90, $3.60
3

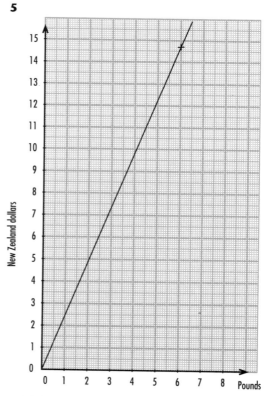

(a) 32 cm², 45 cm², 16 cm², 48 cm²
(b) 6.2 in², 4.2 in², 3.1 in², 3.9 in²

(a) $NZ 4.90, $NZ 15.20, $NZ 9.30, $NZ 13.50
(b) £4.10, £5.10, £3.10, £4.90

6

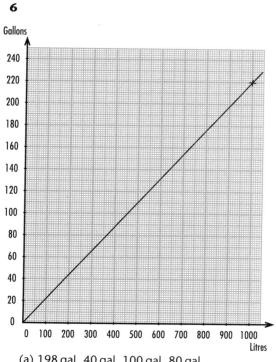

(a) 198 gal, 40 gal, 100 gal, 80 gal
(b) 680 *l*, 410 *l*, 230 *l*, 180 *l*

7

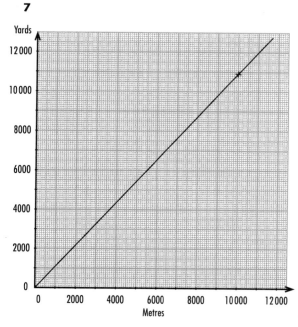

(a) 4600 yd, 7600 yd, 12 000 yd, 8500 yd
(b) 9200 m, 5500 m, 2200 m, 8800 m

8

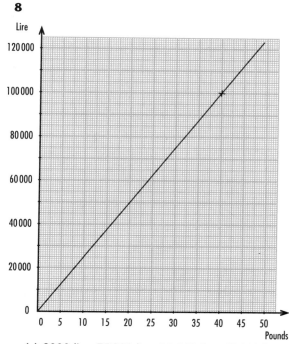

(a) 9000 lire, 75 000 lire, 12 500 lire, 60 000 lire
(b) £36, £4.80, £8, £12

Exercise 54B

1 (a) 185°F, 86°F, 50°F, 100°F
   (b) 35°C, 24°C, 60°C, 11°C
2 (a) $A 1600, $A 1050, $A 800, $A 1260
   (b) £190, £400, £800, £930

3

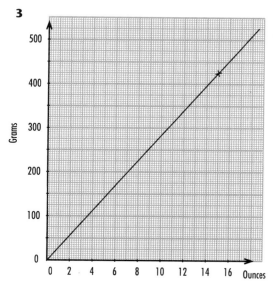

(a) 170 g, 142 g, 255 g, 340 g
(b) 2.8 oz, 7.6 oz, 10.8 oz, 3 oz

4

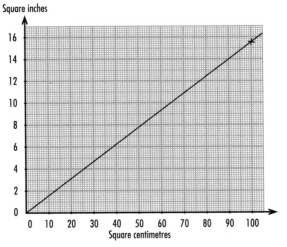

(a) 6.8 in², 5.6 in², 3.4 in², 13.0 in²
(b) 71 cm², 13 cm², 58 cm², 26 cm²

5

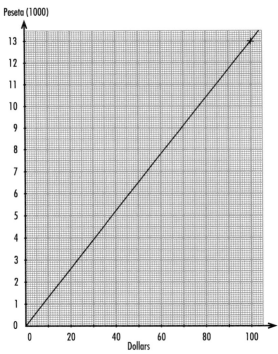

(a) 9100 pta, 5200 pta, 1800 pta, 10 900 pta
(b) $60, $50, $34, $54

6

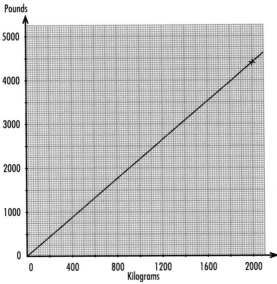

(a) 3300 lb, 2070 lb, 2640 lb, 3960 lb
(b) 1650 kg, 1020 kg, 500 kg, 750 kg

7

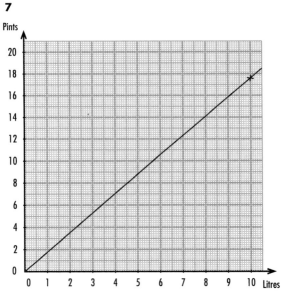

(a) 14.1 pints, 10.2 pints, 7.0 pints, 11.6 pints
(b) 10.2 *l*, 6.8 *l*, 10.8 *l*, 3.4 *l*

8

Kilometres

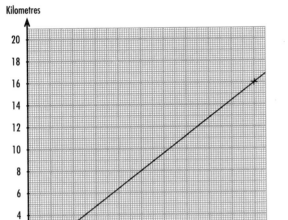

(a) 12 km, 6.1 km, 14.1 km, 8.0 km.
(b) 2.5 miles, 4.0 miles, 3.1 miles, 6.25 miles

13

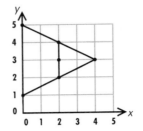

14 Original figures are in italics. Allow some tolerance in answers.

Pounds	Yen
20	3100
40	*6200*
65	*10 000*
58	8990
26	4030
45	*7000*
60	9300
97	*15 000*

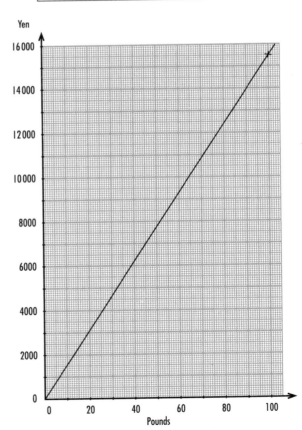

R EVISION

Exercise ▷

1 (a) $f \times g$ (b) $h \times h$ (c) $3 \times f \times g$
   (d) $h \div 5$ (e) $4 \times f \times f$ (f) $3 \times 3 \times e \times e$
   (g) $3 \times f \div 5$ (h) $s \div t$

2 (a) $2x + 8$ (b) $5x - 15$
   (c) $3y + 3$ (d) $20 - 5y$

3 (a) 12   (b) 0   (c) 11   (d) 0

4 (a) 15   (b) 25   (c) 54   (d) 16

5 (a) $w + 5$ (b) $3p$ (c) $\frac{p}{q}$ (d) $10 - r$

6 (a) 0   (b) 0

7 A(1, 4), B(1, 1), C(4, 4), D(4, 1), E(2, 3),
F(5, 3), G(3, 0), H(0, 2)

8 (a) 9°C, 80°C, 20°C, 93°C
   (b) 41°F, 77°F, 122°F, 59°F

Exercise ▷▷

1 5   **2** 30

3 30   **4** 6 cm

5 12   **6** 84 cm

7 8   **8** 12

9 $7w$ **10** $\frac{£C}{3}$

11 $m + 2$

12 (a) 28 cm²   (b) 7

Shape, space and measures

55 ANGLES

Exercise 55A
Measurement of angles is to an accuracy of ±1°.

1	30°	**2**	70°	**3**	55°	**4**	25°
5	41°	**6**	65°	**7**	82°	**8**	135°
9	172°	**10**	67°	**11**	213°	**12**	43°
13	326°	**14**	256°	**15**	154°	**16**	348°

Exercise 55B
Measurement of angles is to an accuracy of ±1°.

1	40°	**2**	10°	**3**	35°	**4**	75°
5	27°	**6**	58°	**7**	24°	**8**	143°
9	160°	**10**	118°	**11**	344°	**12**	63°
13	274°	**14**	242°	**15**	42°	**16**	351°

56 ACCURATE DRAWINGS

Exercises 56A and 56B
Check accuracy of drawing by measuring lines and angles.

57 CONGRUENT SHAPES

Exercise 57A
1 Congruent
2 Not congruent
3 Congruent
4 Not congruent
5 A and B
6 A and C
7 B and C
8 A and D
9 B and D
10 C and D
11 B and C
12 A and C
13/14/15 Check that the sizes of all angles and the lengths of all lines are identical to those shown.

Exercise 57B
1 Not congruent
2 Congruent
3 Not congruent
4 Not congruent
5 A and C
6 A and B
7 C and D
8 B and C
9 B and D
10 C and D
11 A and C
12 A and B
13/14/15 Check that the sizes of all angles and the lengths of all lines are identical to those shown.

58 REFLECTIVE SYMMETRY

Exercise 58A

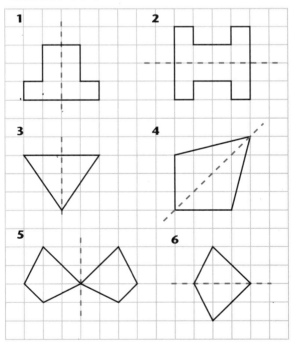

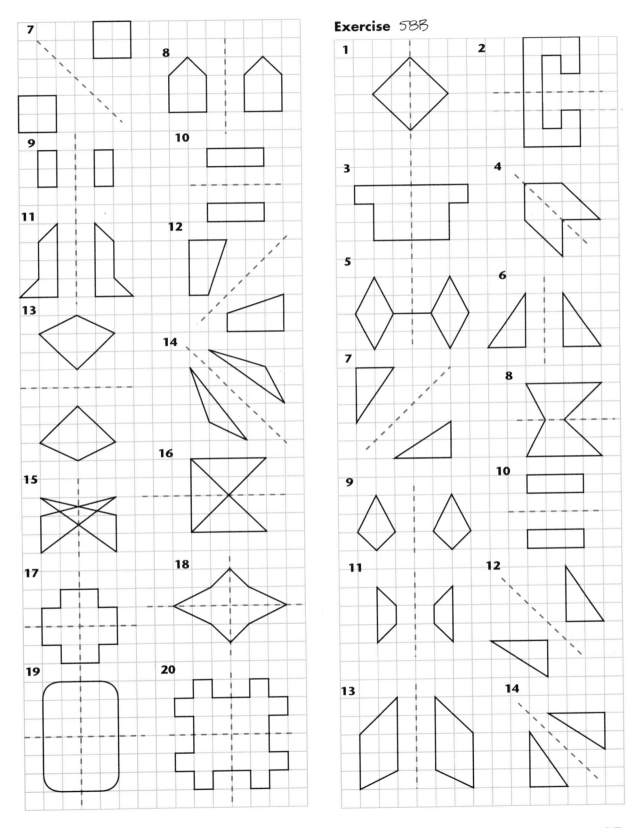

Exercise 58B

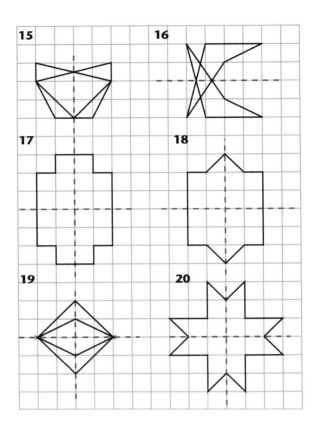

Exercise 59A

1 4		**2** 3		**3** 4		**4** 3	
5 2		**6** 5		**7** 3		**8** None	
9 2		**10** 4		**11** None		**12** 3	

Exercise 59B

1 4		**2** 2		**3** 5		**4** 2	
5 3		**6** 6		**7** 2		**8** 4	
9 8		**10** None		**11** 2		**12** None	

60 IDENTIFYING SYMMETRY

Exercise 60A

1
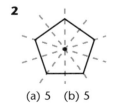

(a) 3   (b) 3

2

(a) 5   (b) 5

3

(a) 4   (b) 4

4

(a) –   (b) 2

5
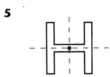

(a) 2   (b) 2

6

(a) 6   (b) 6

7

(a) 1   (b) –

8

(a) 3   (b) 3

9

(a) 1   (b) –

10
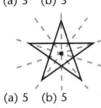

(a) 5   (b) 5

11
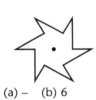

(a) –   (b) 6

12

(a) 3   (b) 3

Exercise 60B

1

(a) 4   (b) 4

2

(a) 2   (b) 2

3

(a) 6   (b) 6

4

(a) 2   (b) 2

5
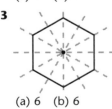

(a) 3   (b) 3

6
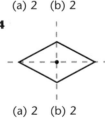

(a) 4   (b) 4

7

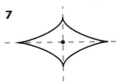

(a) 2   (b) 2

8

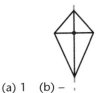

(a) 1   (b) –

9

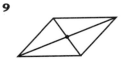

(a) –   (b) 2

10

(a) 3   (b) 3

11

(a) –   (b) 4

12

(a) –   (b) 3

5 Isosceles
7 Corresponding
9 Alternate
11 Equilateral

6 Right-angled
8 Isosceles
10 Supplementary
12 Corresponding

REVISION

Exercise E

1 (a) W and Y   (b) W and X   (c) X and Y
    (d) Y and Z

2 (a)(i) 6 (ii) 6   (b)(i) 1 (ii) 0

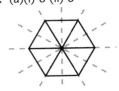

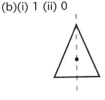

(c)(i) 8 (ii) 8   (d)(i) 2 (ii) 2

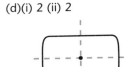

(e)(i) 0 (ii) 4   (f)(i) 3 (ii) 3

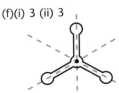

(g)(i) 7 (ii) 7   (h)(i) 0 (ii) 5

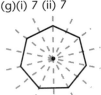

3 (a) Obtuse   (b) Acute   (c) Acute
    (d) Reflex   (e) Obtuse   (f) Reflex

4 (a) Equilateral   (b) Supplementary
    (c) Isosceles   (d) Right-angled
    (e) Alternate   (f) Isosceles
    (g) Equilateral   (h) Corresponding

Exercise EE

1 Measurement is to an accuracy of ±1°.
    (a) 35°   (b) 305°   (c) 210°   (d) 75°
2 Check accuracy of drawing by measuring angles.
3 Check accuracy of drawing by measuring lines
    and angles.

61   GEOMETRIC DESCRIPTIONS

Exercise 61A

1 Acute	**2** Obtuse	**3** Reflex
4 Acute	**5** Acute	**6** Obtuse
7 Obtuse	**8** Acute	**9** Obtuse
10 Obtuse	**11** Obtuse	**12** Reflex
13 Reflex	**14** Acute	**15** Acute
16 Acute	**17** Reflex	**18** Reflex
19 Obtuse	**20** Reflex	

Exercise 61B

1 Acute	**2** Reflex	**3** Acute
4 Reflex	**5** Acute	**6** Obtuse
7 Obtuse	**8** Acute	**9** Obtuse
10 Reflex	**11** Obtuse	**12** Acute
13 Reflex	**14** Obtuse	**15** Reflex
16 Acute	**17** Acute	**18** Obtuse
19 Acute	**20** Obtuse	

Exercise 61C

1 Right-angled	**2** Supplementary
3 Alternate	**4** Equilateral
5 Right-angled	**6** Corresponding
7 Isosceles	**8** Alternate
9 Equilateral	**10** Supplementary
11 Isosceles	**12** Corresponding

Exercise 61D

1 Supplementary	**2** Alternate
3 Equilateral	**4** Right-angled

4 (a)

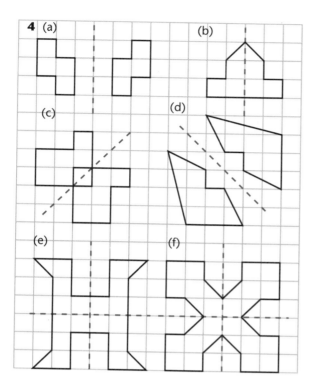

5 (a) 2   (b) 4   (c) 3   (d) 5   (e) 4
   (f) 2   (g) 4   (h) 2

62 METRIC UNITS

Exercise 62A

1 80 mm	**2** 600 cm	**3** 0.067 km
4 2.65 cm	**5** 1.35 kg	**6** 420 ml
7 1470 g	**8** 160 cl	**9** 7000 m
10 1.53 m	**11** 50 ml	**12** 4000 kg
13 0.6 g	**14** 0.7 *l*	**15** 0.4 t
16 0.007 kg	**17** 54.2 cm	**18** 50 ml
19 124.1 mm	**20** 471 cm	

Exercise 62B

1 0.029 km	**2** 7.15 cm	**3** 50 mm
4 840 ml	**5** 300 cm	**6** 2.55 kg
7 460 cl	**8** 2520 g	**9** 2.98 m
10 800 ml	**11** 6000 m	**12** 3500 kg
13 0.25 g	**14** 15.1 mm	**15** 303 cm
16 0.35 *l*	**17** 149 cm	**18** 0.9 t
19 0.008 kg	**20** 140 ml	

Exercise 62C

1 0.325 *l*	**2** 1.35 *l*	**3** 4.47 m	**4** 0.89 kg
5 150	**6** 1.4 *l*	**7** 1250	**8** 40
9 7 kg	**10** 47.7 kg		

Exercise 62D

1 43 m	**2** 9.5 t	**3** 15.5 *l*	**4** 4.26 kg
5 33	**6** 75 *l*	**7** 3550 m	**8** 4725 g
9 57.5 kg	**10** 28.8 m		

63 SENSIBLE ESTIMATES

Exercise 63A

1 J	**2** D	**3** M	**4** G	**5** B
6 N	**7** Q	**8** K	**9** R	**10** T
11 C	**12** F	**13** I	**14** S	**15** A
16 L	**17** O	**18** E	**19** P	**20** H

Exercise 63B

1 K	**2** E	**3** J	**4** L	**5** O
6 B	**7** P	**8** F	**9** R	**10** A
11 G	**12** N	**13** S	**14** T	**15** Q
16 C	**17** H	**18** M	**19** D	**20** I

64 IMPERIAL UNITS

Exercise 64A

1 6 ft $1\frac{1}{2}$ in	**2** $10\frac{1}{2}$ ft	**3** 8 st 13 lb
4 67 oz	**5** 14 pt	**6** 1799 yd
7 12 oz	**8** 5 ft 10 in	**9** 5 ft 5 in
10 11 ft	**11** 1100 yd	**12** 14 st 4 lb
13 10 ft	**14** 47 in	**15** 51 oz
16 9 in	**17** 8 yd 1 ft	**18** 5 fl. oz
19 $6\frac{1}{2}$ cwt	**20** 2 ft $10\frac{1}{4}$ in	

Exercise 64B

1 4 ft	**2** 3 gal 1 pt	
3 1 mile 1240 yd	**4** 39 in	**5** 8 st 3 lb
6 40 in	**7** 145 lb	**8** 60 fl. oz
9 75 in	**10** 22 ft	**11** 64 cwt
12 53 in	**13** 15 fl. oz	**14** 13 ft
15 68 oz	**16** 27 in	**17** 18 pt
18 88 in	**19** 4 ft 2 in	**20** 5680 yd

Exercise 64C

1 16 st	**2** 23 lb 8 oz	**3** 9 in
4 2 ft 8 in	**5** $4\frac{3}{4}$ oz	**6** 2 lb 6 oz
7 8 yd 2 ft	**8** 13 gal 6 pt	**9** 40
10 11 st 11 lb		

Exercise 64D

1 33 gal	**2** 7 ft 4 in	**3** 10 lb 4 oz
4 3 lb 14 oz	**5** 6 gal 1 pt	**6** 52 yd
7 260 yd	**8** 13 gal 1 pt	**9** $5\frac{1}{4}$ in
10 2 gal 4 pt		

65 METRIC AND IMPERIAL EQUIVALENTS

Exercise 65A
1 44 lb
2 30 cm
3 16 km
4 9 l
5 9 kg
6 14 pt
7 90 cm
8 10 miles
9 56 km
10 3.5 m
11 $27\frac{1}{2}$ miles
12 16 l
13 $2\frac{1}{2}$ ft
14 10.5 kg
15 10 in
16 210 cm
17 35 pt
18 5 yd
19 5 in
20 110 lb

Exercise 65B
1 32 km
2 66 lb
3 120 cm
4 32 l
5 45 cm
6 20 miles
7 6 kg
8 13 l
9 21 pt
10 7.5 m
11 $1\frac{1}{2}$ ft
12 14 in
13 240 cm
14 90 cm
15 15.5 kg
16 $37\frac{1}{2}$ miles
17 $6\frac{1}{2}$ yd
18 28 pt
19 6 in
20 72 km

Exercise 65C
1 90 cm
2 2 m
3 a; 4 kg ≈ 8.8 lb
4 6.136 kg
5 8.8 oz
6 $207\frac{1}{2}$ mile
7 6.56 gal
8 15 cm
9 $168\frac{3}{4}$ miles
10 205.7 l

Exercise 65D
1 12 m
2 17.6 lb
3 a; 3 kg ≈ 6.6 lb
4 8.4 m
5 6 ft
6 14.08 oz
7 112 km
8 $8\frac{3}{4}$ gal
9 237.5 cm
10 10 m

66 SCALES

Exercise 66A
1 (a) 10 km
   (b) 25 km
   (c) 32 km
   (d) 8 km
2 (a) 300 m
   (b) 40 m
   (c) 170 m
   (d) 360 m
3 (a) 40 km
   (b) 56 km
   (c) 28 km
   (d) 70 km
4 (a) 16 m
   (b) 4.8 m
   (c) 9.6 m
   (d) 15.2 m
5 (a) 6 m
   (b) 13.2 m
   (c) 20.4 m
   (d) 4.2 m
6 (a) 20 km
   (b) 3 km
   (c) 9.5 km
   (d) 11.5 km
7 (a) 90 m
   (b) 15 m
   (c) 87 m
   (d) 111 m
8 (a) 50 km
   (b) 97.5 km
   (c) 37.5 km
   (d) 7.5 km

Exercise 66B
1 (a) 30 km
   (b) 2 km
   (c) 21 km
   (d) 36 km
2 (a) 8 km
   (b) 6 km
   (c) 10.4 km
   (d) 13.2 km
3 (a) 20 m
   (b) 0.5 m
   (c) 8 m
   (d) 13.5 m
4 (a) 20 km
   (b) 62 km
   (c) 56 km
   (d) 44 km
5 (a) 50 m
   (b) 22.5 m
   (c) 77.5 m
   (d) 40 m
6 (a) 8 m
   (b) 19.2 m
   (c) 23.3 m
   (d) 29.6 m
7 (a) 450 km
   (b) 165 km
   (c) 360 km
   (d) 525 km
8 (a) 280 m
   (b) 28 m
   (c) 126 m
   (d) 224 m

Exercise 66C

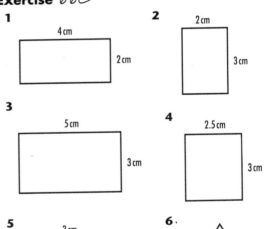

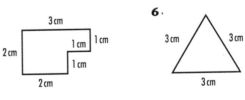

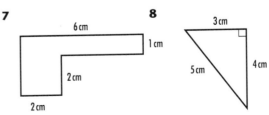

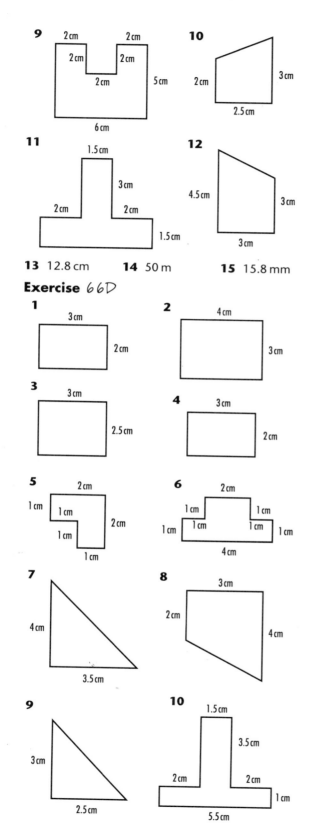

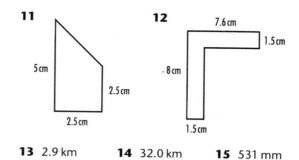

9 2 cm 2 cm / 2 cm 2 cm / 2 cm / 5 cm / 6 cm

10 2 cm / 3 cm / 2.5 cm

11 1.5 cm / 3 cm / 2 cm 2 cm / 1.5 cm

12 4.5 cm / 3 cm / 3 cm

13 12.8 cm **14** 50 m **15** 15.8 mm

Exercise 66D

1 3 cm / 2 cm

2 4 cm / 3 cm

3 3 cm / 2.5 cm

4 3 cm / 2 cm

5 2 cm / 1 cm / 1 cm / 2 cm / 1 cm / 1 cm

6 2 cm / 1 cm / 1 cm / 1 cm / 1 cm / 1 cm / 1 cm / 4 cm

7 4 cm / 3.5 cm

8 3 cm / 2 cm / 4 cm

9 3 cm / 2.5 cm

10 1.5 cm / 3.5 cm / 2 cm / 2 cm / 1 cm / 5.5 cm

11 5 cm / 2.5 cm / 2.5 cm

12 7.6 cm / 1.5 cm / 8 cm / 1.5 cm

13 2.9 km **14** 32.0 km **15** 531 mm

67 AREA AND PERIMETER

Exercise 67A

1 (a) 12 cm (b) 9 cm²
2 (a) 8 cm (b) 3 cm²
3 (a) 10 cm (b) 6 cm²
4 (a) 10 cm (b) 4 cm²
5 (a) 8 cm (b) 3 cm²
6 (a) 10 cm (b) 5 cm²
7 (a) 12 cm (b) 5 cm²
8 (a) 12 cm (b) 7 cm²
9 (a) 12 cm (b) 5 cm²
10 (a) 18 cm (b) 10 cm²
11 (a) 20 cm (b) 13 cm²
12 (a) 24 cm (b) 11 cm²
13 (a) 14 cm (b) 12 cm²
14 (a) 20 cm (b) 25 cm²
15 (a) 20 cm (b) 24 cm²
16 (a) 20 cm (b) 21 cm²
17 (a) 20 cm (b) 18 cm²
18 (a) 28 cm (b) 36 cm²
19 (a) 46 cm (b) 60 cm²
20 (a) 22 cm (b) 18 cm²

Exercise 67B

1 (a) 6 cm (b) 2 cm²
2 (a) 12 cm (b) 8 cm²
3 (a) 8 cm (b) 3 cm²
4 (a) 8 cm (b) 4 cm²
5 (a) 14 cm (b) 6 cm²
6 (a) 10 cm (b) 4 cm²·
7 (a) 14 cm (b) 6 cm²
8 (a) 14 cm (b) 6 cm²
9 (a) 14 cm (b) 6 cm²
10 (a) 14 cm (b) 10 cm²
11 (a) 18 cm (b) 12 cm²
12 (a) 16 cm (b) 7 cm²
13 (a) 18 cm (b) 20 cm²
14 (a) 24 cm (b) 36 cm²
15 (a) 16 cm (b) 12 cm²

16 (a) 22 cm   (b) 28 cm²
17 (a) 26 cm   (b) 22 cm²
18 (a) 28 cm   (b) 27 cm²
19 (a) 32 cm   (b) 39 cm²
20 (a) 34 cm   (b) 49 cm²

68 VOLUME

Exercise 68A

1 16 cm³	**2** 8 cm³	**3** 6 m³	**4** 12 cm³
5 10 cm³	**6** 11 cm³	**7** 9 cm³	**8** 18 cm³
9 12 cm³	**10** 18 cm³	**11** 17 cm³	**12** 36 cm³
13 40 cm³	**14** 54 cm³	**15** 72 cm³	**16** 100 cm³

Exercise 68B

1 8 cm³	**2** 9 cm³	**3** 8 cm³	**4** 10 cm³
5 10 cm³	**6** 13 cm³	**7** 12 cm³	**8** 12 cm³
9 14 cm³	**10** 9 cm³	**11** 12 cm³	**12** 15 cm³
13 36 cm³	**14** 80 cm³	**15** 52 cm³	**16** 100 cm³

R EVISION

Exercise F

1 (a) 3000 m   (b) 0.045 kg   (c) 4780 kg
   (d) 0.4 g   (e) 0.15 t   (f) 6.32 m
   (g) 0.184 km   (h) 30 mm   (i) 0.8 *l*
   (j) 650 cm   (k) 430 cl

2 (a) 730 ml   (b) 3000 mg   (c) 2 t 10 cwt
   (d) 11 st 1 lb   (e) 5 gal   (f) 2 lb 6 oz
   (g) 0.427 *l*   (h) 69 oz   (i) 17 miles 80 yd
   (j) 1 cwt 18 lb   (k) 10 ft 5 in   (l) 162 lb

3 (a) 13 yd 1 ft   (b) 38 pt   (c) $5\frac{1}{4}$ gal
   (d) 40 miles   (e) 110 lb   (f) 20 *l*
   (g) 24 km   (h) 240 cm   (i) 50 kg
   (j) 225 cm   (k) 30 kg   (l) $12\frac{1}{4}$ gal

4 (a) (i) 30 km   (ii) 17 km   (iii) 23 km
     (iv) 8 km
   (b) (i) 16 m   (ii) 4 m   (iii) 29.6 m
     (iv) 20.8 m
   (c) (i) 250 mm   (ii) 875 mm   (iii) 700 mm
     (iv) 350 mm

5 (a)

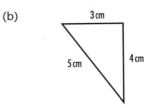

(b)

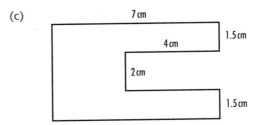

(c)

6 (a) (i) 14 cm   (ii) 10 cm²
   (b) (i) 16 cm   (ii) 16 cm²
   (c) (i) 16 cm   (ii) 7 cm²
   (d) (i) 18 cm   (ii) 12 cm²
   (e) (i) 18 cm   (ii) 8 cm²

7 (a) 27 cm³   (b) 20 cm³   (c) 32 cm³   (d) 76 cm³

Exercise FF

1 6.62 m
2 2.94 kg
3 748 kg
4 1.2 m
5 3.36 kg
6 27.5 *l*
7 11 st
8 1100 yd
9 9 gal 7 pt
10 1 ton 5 cwt
11 8 ft
12 8 gal 2 pt
13 42 in
14 5 ft 4 in
15 200 kg
16 28.1875 gal
17 10 st 5.4 lb
18 3.2 m
19 5.48 m
20 25 m
21 (a) 44 m   (b) 88 tiles   (c) 22 tiles

Handling data

Exercise 69A

1 (a) 4   (b) 3   (c) 1, 6   (d) 37
2 (a) (i) £18 000 (ii) £10 000 (iii) £7000
     (b) 1997–1998   (c) (i) £4000 (ii) £5000
3 (a) Jamaica   (b) Paris   (c) (i) $8\frac{1}{2}$ h (ii) 7 h
4 (a) (i) 3 (ii) 4   (b) 100–150 g   (c) 50–100 g
5 (a) (i) 60% (ii) 65% (iii) 65%
     (b) (i) October (ii) February and September
     (c) August 75%
6 (a) 16   (b) 9–10 a.m.
     (c) 10–11 a.m., 2–3 p.m.
7 (a) (i) 13 (ii) 28   (b) 190 and 200 cm
     (c) 150 and 160 cm
8 (a) (i) 2100 (ii) 1900 (iii) 2500
     (b) 3 and 6   (c) (i) 2800 (ii) 1200
9 (a) (i) 13°C (ii) 12°C (iii) 19°C
     (b) 4 min, $8\frac{1}{2}$ min, 24 min
     (c) (i) $27\frac{1}{2}$ min, 25°C (ii) 20 min, $4\frac{1}{2}$°C
10 (a) 19   (b) (i) 45 (ii) 68   (c) 28

Exercise 69B

1 (a) 3   (b) 5   (c) 4   (d) 27
2 (a) Saturday   (b) (i) 10 mm (ii) $12\frac{1}{2}$ min
     (c) Tuesday, Sunday   (d) Thursday
3 (a) 1989   (b) 1987, 1988, 1990
     (c) (i) £17 m (ii) £15 m (iii) £16 m
4 (a) (i) 11 (ii) 6   (b) 1 m and 2 m   (c) 39
5 (a) Saturday   (b) Thursday and Friday
     (c) (i) 2 (ii) 4
6 (a) 260   (b) Days 3 and 4
     (c) (i) 300 (ii) 380   (d) 60
7 (a) (i) 7 (ii) 4   (b) 9 kg and 10 kg
     (c) (i) 9 (ii) 19
8 (a) (i) £43 (ii) £34   (b) (i) Week 6 (ii) Week 8
     (c) £32
9 (a) (i) 150 rev/s (ii) 240 rev/s   (b) 5 s, 13 s, 27 s
     (c) (i) 280 rev/s (ii) 100 rev/s
10 (a) 20 *l* and 30 *l*   (b) (i) 22 (ii) 12
     (c) (i) 63 (ii) 35

Exercise 70A

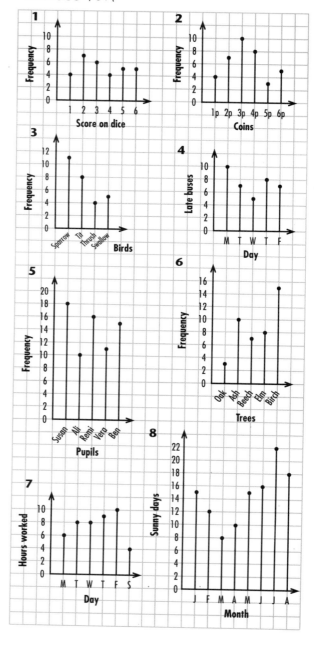

Exercise 70B

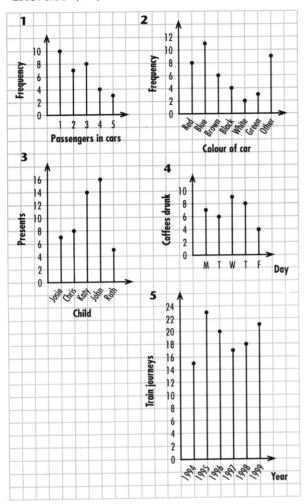

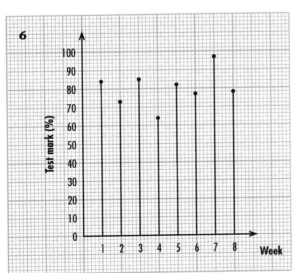

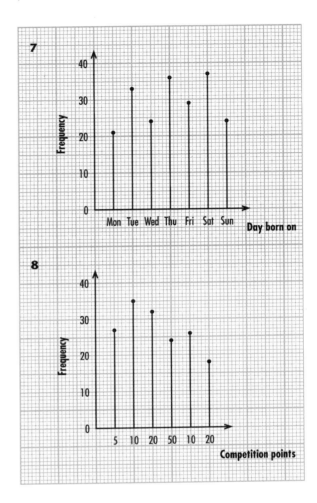

71 DRAWING LINE GRAPHS

Exercise 71A

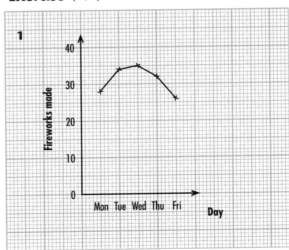

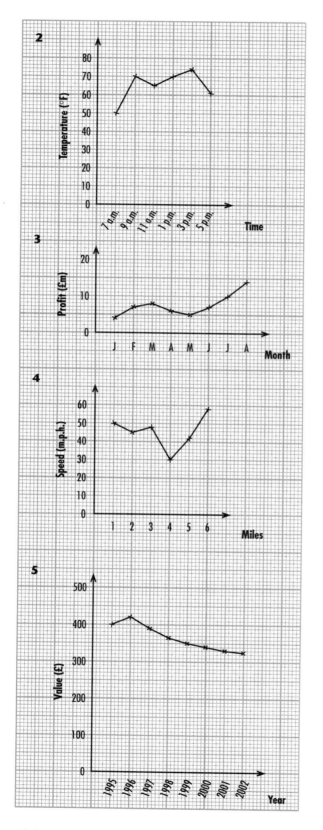

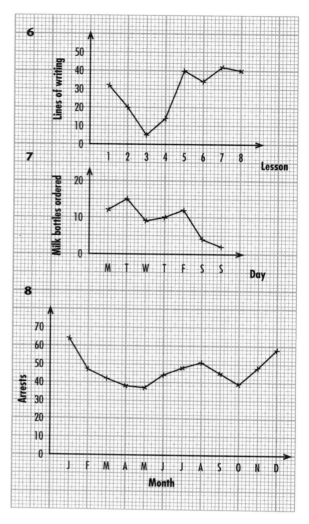

Exercise 71B

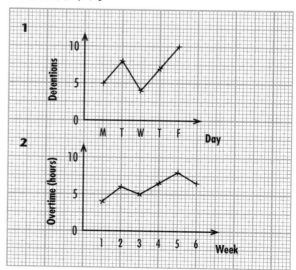

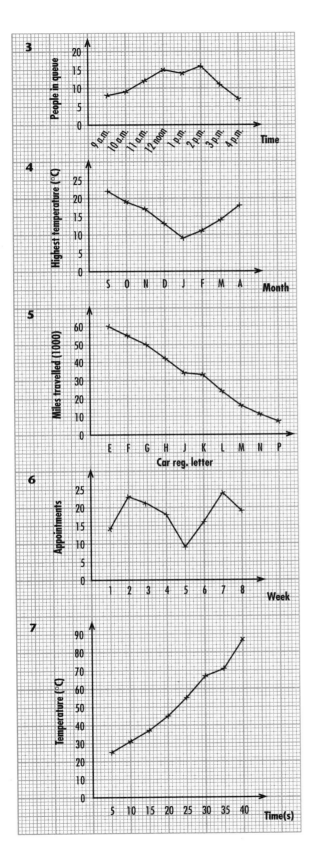

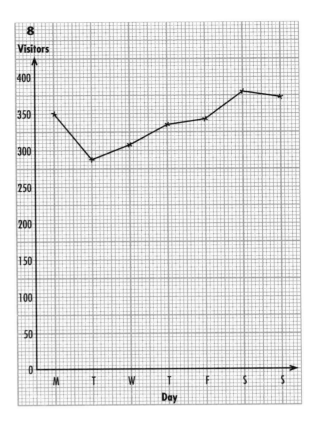

72 GROUPING DATA

Exercise 72A

1 (a)

Animals	Frequency
0–9	3
10–19	5
20–29	7
30–39	8
40–49	6
50–59	4
60–69	2
Total	35

(b)

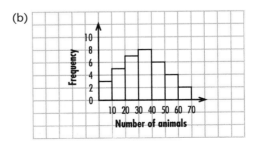

2 (a)

Deliveries made	Frequency
0–9	4
10–19	7
20–29	9
30–39	5
40–49	5
50–59	3
60–69	2
Total	35

(b)

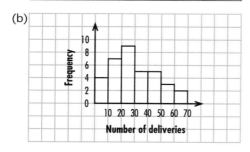

3 (a)

Defects	Frequency
0–4	5
5–9	6
10–14	7
15–19	5
20–24	3
25–29	3
30–34	1
Total	30

(b)

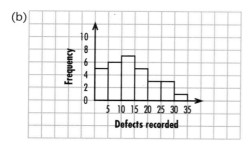

4 (a)

Living relatives	Frequency
0–4	2
5–9	6
10–14	8
15–19	6
20–24	4
25–29	4
Total	30

(b)

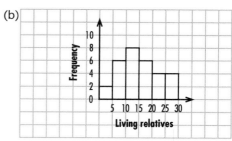

5 (a)

Customers	Frequency
0–4	2
5–9	5
10–14	11
15–19	13
20–24	4
Total	35

(b)

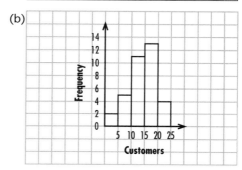

6 (a)

Cars in car-park	Frequency
0–49	1
50–99	2
100–149	5
150–199	11
200–249	14
250–299	8
300–349	3
350–399	1
Total	45

(b)

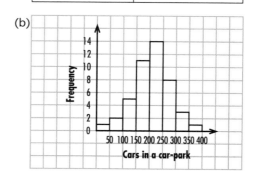

7 (a)

Money recorded	Frequency
£0.00–£9.99	2
£10.00–£19.99	8
£20.00–£29.99	5
£30.00–£39.99	7
£40.00–£49.99	10
£50.00–£59.99	3
Total	35

(b)

(b)
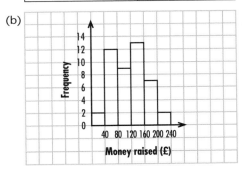

10 (a)

Money raised	Frequency
£0.00–£39.99	2
£40.00–£79.99	12
£80.00–£119.99	9
£120.00–£159.99	13
£160.00–£199.99	7
£200.00–£239.99	2
Total	45

(b)
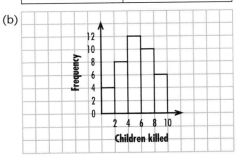

8 (a)

Attendance	Frequency
0–24	1
25–49	2
50–74	1
75–99	3
100–124	8
125–149	12
150–174	10
175–199	3
Total	40

(b)
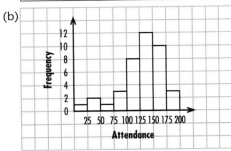

Exercise 72B

1 (a)

Children killed	Frequency
1–2	4
3–4	8
5–6	12
7–8	10
9–10	6
Total	40

(b)

9 (a)

Typing speed	Frequency
21–30	2
31–40	5
41–50	10
51–60	14
61–70	9
71–80	4
81–90	1
Total	45

2 (a)

Test marks	Frequency
0–9	1
10–19	2
20–29	3
30–39	6
40–49	7
50–59	9
60–69	2
Total	30

(b)

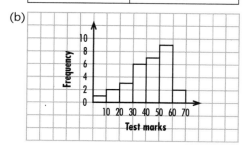

3 (a)

Money spent	Frequency
£0.00–£0.99	6
£1.00–£1.99	9
£2.00–£2.99	12
£3.00–£3.99	2
£4.00–£4.99	2
£5.00–£5.99	1
Total	32

(b)

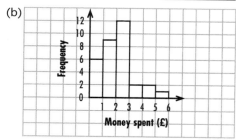

4 (a)

IQ scores	Frequency
81–85	1
86–90	3
91–95	3
96–100	5
101–105	8
106–110	6
111–115	4
116–120	2
Total	32

(b)

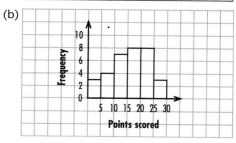

5 (a)

Points	Frequency
0–4	3
5–9	4
10–14	7
15–19	8
20–24	8
25–29	3
Total	33

(b)

6 (a)

Annual income	Frequency
0–3999	1
4000–7999	4
8000–11 999	9
12 000–15 999	11
16 000–19 999	8
20 000–23 999	3
Total	36

(b)

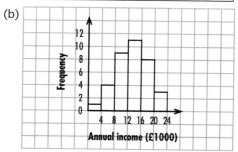

7 (a)

Typing speed	Frequency
21–30	2
31–40	1
41–50	3
51–60	9
61–70	9
71–80	12
81–90	4
Total	40

(b)

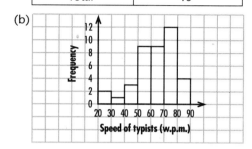

8 (a)

Number of tins	Frequency
400–449	1
450–499	3
500–549	10
550–599	8
600–649	12
650–699	7
700–749	4
Total	45

(b)

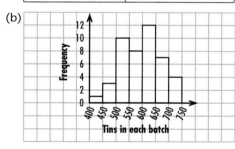

9 (a)

Items	Frequency
0–40	3
41–80	7
81–120	12
121–160	9
161–200	10
201–240	6
241–280	3
Total	50

(b)

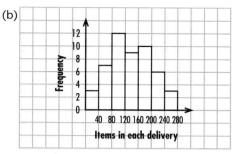

10 (a)

Marks	Frequency
10–19	2
20–29	2
30–39	3
40–49	5
50–59	12
60–69	7
70–79	11
80–89	6
90–99	2
Total	50

(b)

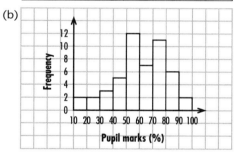

73 INTERPRETING PIE CHARTS

Exercise 73A

1 (a) Heating   (b) Twice as much
2 (a) House   (b) Other   (c) 25
   (d) Flat and bungalow
3 (a) White   (b) Brown   (c) Brown
4 (a) (i) $\frac{1}{6}$ (ii) $\frac{1}{4}$ (b) 60+
   (c) 10–20, 40–60
5 (a) UK   (b) Other   (c) Africa and Asia
6 (a) Europe   (b) America, Asia   (c) £20m
7 (a) $\frac{1}{4}$ (b) Ist class   (c) 2nd class
8 (a) Bus   (b) Cycle   (c) Cycle   (d) $\frac{1}{4}$

Exercise 73B

1 (a) Maths   (b) IT   (c) Science
2 (a) Entertainment   (b) Scientific   (c) $\frac{1}{4}$
3 (a) Dog   (b) (i) 10   (ii) 5   (c) Fish, mice
4 (a) Choc ices and ice-cream tubs
    (b) Lollies   (c) $\frac{3}{8}$
5 (a) Rugby   (b) Swimming   (c) Golf
6 (a) Pass   (b) Credit   (c) 25
7 (a) Form time   (b) Lessons
8 (a) Salt and vinegar, beef
    (b) Cheese and onion
    (c) (i) Beef   (ii) Cheese and onion

REVISION

Exercise G

1
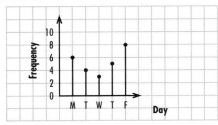

2
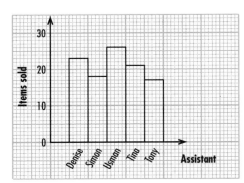

3
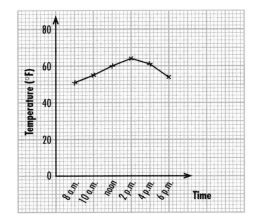

4

Points	Frequency
0–4	3
5–9	6
10–14	12
15–19	8
20–24	7
25–29	4
Total	40

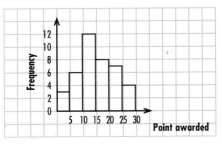

5

Marks	Frequency
0–9.9	4
10–19.9	7
20–29.9	10
30–39.9	11
40–49.9	5
50–59.9	3
Total	40

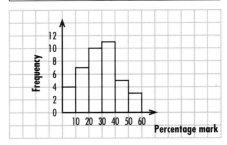

Exercise GG

1 (a) £800   (b) £2300
    (c) (i) Thursday Week 1 (ii) Monday Week 2
       (iii) Thursday Week 2
    (d) (i) £1100   (ii) £1800   (iii) £1700
    (e) (i) Increase of £300   (ii) Decrease of £200
       (iii) Decrease of £100

2 (a) (i) 35°C   (ii) 50°C   (iii) 64°C
    (b) (i) 60 s   (ii) 70 s   (iii) 25 s
    (c) (i) $17\frac{1}{2}$°C   (ii) $8\frac{1}{2}$°C

3 (a)

Passengers	Frequency
0–4	2
5–9	3
10–14	8
15–19	11
20–24	13
25–29	9
Total	46

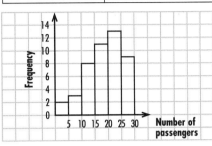

(b) 20–24   (c) 5   (d) 22   (e) 46

4 (a) Icing and castor sugar   (b) Brown   (c) 9

74 MODE AND MEDIAN

Exercise 74A

1 (a) 5   (b) 4   **2** (a) 3   (b) $4\frac{1}{2}$
3 (a) 5   (b) 4   **4** (a) 17   (b) $17\frac{1}{2}$
5 (a) 2   (b) 3   **6** (a) 10   (b) 10
7 (a) 81   (b) 75   **8** (a) 21   (b) 49
9 (a) 36   (b) 34   **10** (a) 9   (b) $11\frac{1}{2}$
11 (a) 4   (b) 5   **12** (a) 2   (b) 5
13 (a) 2   (b) 2   **14** (a) 22   (b) 23
15 (a) 3   (b) 3

Exercise 74B

1 (a) 2   (b) 3   **2** (a) 7   (b) $5\frac{1}{2}$
3 (a) 11   (b) 12   **4** (a) 35   (b) 31
5 (a) 6   (b) 5   **6** (a) 3   (b) 7
7 (a) 25   (b) 23   **8** (a) 50   (b) 54
9 (a) 5   (b) 4   **10** (a) 8   (b) 9
11 (a) 22   (b) 21   **12** (a) 45   (b) 41
13 (a) 1   (b) 1   **14** (a) 19   (b) $19\frac{1}{2}$
15 (a) 12   (b) $11\frac{1}{2}$

75 MEAN AND RANGE

Exercise 75A

1 (a) 3   (b) 5   **2** (a) 2.5   (b) 5
3 (a) 15   (b) 12   **4** (a) 62   (b) 2

5 (a) 3   (b) 3   **6** (a) 101.2   (b) 157
7 (a) 3.8   (b) 8   **8** (a) 18   (b) 14
9 (a) 17.2   (b) 30   **10** (a) 6.7   (b) 8
11 (a) 2.3   (b) 3   **12** (a) 2.1   (b) 3
13 (a) 39.5   (b) 7   **14** (a) 70.25   (b) 17
15 (a) 4.6   (b) 8   **16** (a) 15   (b) 8
17 (a) 30.1   (b) 27   **18** (a) 68   (b) 100
19 (a) 52.4   (b) 80   **20** (a) 56   (b) 82

Exercise 75B

1 (a) 2   (b) 4   **2** (a) 4   (b) 5
3 (a) 3   (b) 5   **4** (a) 4   (b) 7
5 (a) 121.8   (b) 44   **6** (a) 12.6   (b) 12
7 (a) 6.9   (b) 8   **8** (a) 9   (b) 12
9 (a) 73.25   (b) 17   **10** (a) 29.5   (b) 27
11 (a) 2.1   (b) 4   **12** (a) 72.25   (b) 11
13 (a) 40.25   (b) 7   **14** (a) 66.9   (b) 100
15 (a) 6   (b) 6   **16** (a) 21.5   (b) 33
17 (a) 68   (b) 110   **18** (a) 162   (b) 470
19 (a) 148.8   (b) 545   **20** (a) 69.5   (b) 110

76 USING THE MEAN AND RANGE

Exercise 76A

1 30   **2** £27.20
3 315   **4** 84
5 3   **6** 1
7 5
8 6.33, 6.63; Valerie
9 27, 25; Class TR
10 442.9, 476.11; Neptune
11 60.15, 57.73; Boys
12 2.1, 2.125; Tigers
13 63.83, 64.25; Serafim
14 17.5, 18.2; Susan
15 60.25, 60.16; Lynn

Exercise 76B

1 72   **2** 15.6 kg
3 476   **4** 108
5 6   **6** 9
7 2
8 15.86, 13; Group A
9 12.67, 11.43; Pat
10 145, 152; Browns
11 70.9, 69; Crest Club
12 15.9, 13.0; Ben
13 83.7, 83.2; Blackpool
14 19.5, 19.7; Hard Hits
15 6.75, 7.1; Sally

77 PROBABILITY SCALE

Exercise 77A

1 E	**2** A	**3** E	**4** F	**5** I
6 C	**7** B	**8** G	**9** F	**10** A
11 E	**12** I	**13** H	**14** D	**15** I
16 D	**17** A	**18** G	**19** E	**20** B

Exercise 77B

1 E	**2** I	**3** C	**4** A	**5** G
6 E	**7** F	**8** A	**9** H	**10** I
11 D	**12** G	**13** B	**14** C	**15** A
16 F	**17** E	**18** I	**19** B	**20** H

78 OUTCOMES

Exercise 78A

1 a e i o u

2 11 12 13 14 15 16 21 22 23 24 25 26 31 32 33 34 35 36 41 42 43 44 45 46 51 52 53 54 55 56 61 62 63 64 65 66

3 H T

4 1 2 3 4 5 6 7 8

5 A C E H I M S T

6 3 4 5

7 2H 4H 6H 8H 2T 4T 6T 8T

8 A3 A5 A7 B3 B5 B7 C3 C5 C7

9 1X 2X 3X 4X 1Y 2Y 3Y 4Y 1Z 2Z 3Z 4Z

10 HHHH HHHT HHTH HTHH THHH HTTH TTHH HTTH HHTT HTHT THTH THHT TTTT TTTH TTHT THTT HTTT

11 BlackA BlackB BlackC WhiteA WhiteB WhiteC

12 BB RR GG YY BR BG BY RB RG RY GB GR GY YB YR YG

13 RRR GGG BBB RRG RGR GRR RRB RBR BRR GGR GRG RGG GGB GBG BGG BBR RBB BRB BBG GBB BGB RGB RBG GRB GBR BRG BGR

Exercise 78B

1 V W X Y Z

2 1 2 3 4 5 6

3 HHH HTT THT TTH TTT HHT THH HTH

4 2 4 6 8 10 12 14 16 18 20 22 24

5 1 3 5 7 9 11

6 I M P S

7 3H 4H 5H 3T 4T 5T

8 2 4 6 8

9 EW ES EN WS WN SN

10 1H 2H 3H 4H 5H 6H 7H 8H 1T 2T 3T 4T 5T 6T 7T 8T

11 BRG BRY BGY RGY BBR BBG BBY RRB RRG RRY GGB GGR GGY YYB YYR YYG

12 YYY YWP YPW WPY WYP PYW PWY WWP WPW PWW WWY WYW YWW YYP YPY PYY YYW YWY WYY PPY PYP YPP PPW PWP WPP WWW PPP

13 BBB BBW BWB WBB WWB WBW BWW WWW

79 PROBABILITY FRACTIONS

Exercise 79A

1 $\frac{1}{6}$	**2** $\frac{1}{2}$	**3** $\frac{1}{10}$	**4** $\frac{1}{7}$
5 $\frac{1}{5}$	**6** $\frac{1}{12}$	**7** $\frac{1}{250}$	**8** $\frac{1}{7}$
9 $\frac{1}{5}$	**10** $\frac{1}{3}$	**11** $\frac{1}{6}$	**12** $\frac{1}{8}$
13 $\frac{1}{7}$	**14** $\frac{1}{8}$	**15** $\frac{1}{1000}$	**16** $\frac{1}{31}$
17 $\frac{1}{6}$	**18** $\frac{1}{4}$	**19** $\frac{1}{28}$	**20** $\frac{1}{2}$

Exercise 79B

1 $\frac{1}{2}$	**2** $\frac{1}{7}$	**3** $\frac{1}{200}$	**4** $\frac{1}{20}$
5 $\frac{1}{6}$	**6** $\frac{1}{12}$	**7** $\frac{1}{5}$	**8** $\frac{1}{2}$
9 $\frac{1}{9}$	**10** $\frac{1}{8}$	**11** $\frac{1}{6}$	**12** $\frac{1}{7}$
13 $\frac{1}{6}$	**14** $\frac{1}{5000}$	**15** $\frac{1}{5}$	**16** $\frac{1}{7}$
17 $\frac{1}{30}$	**18** $\frac{1}{20}$	**19** $\frac{1}{30}$	**20** $\frac{1}{5}$

R EVISION

Exercise H

1 (a) (i) 8 (ii) 7.46 (iii) 9
  (b) (i) 3 (ii) 3.13 (iii) 4
  (c) (i) 43.5 (ii) 43.79 (iii) 6
  (d) (i) 3 (ii) 3 (iii) 7
  (e) (i) 22 (ii) 21.47 (iii) 7
  (f) (i) 22 (ii) 21.6 (iii) 27

2 70 **3** 76.5

4 14 **5** 6

Exercise HH

1 Gary (3.67, 3.77)   **2** Rangers (7, 8.83)

3 Brian (8.15, 8.33)

4 (a) E   (b) A   (c) C   (d) I   (e) F

5 (a) H1 H2 H3 H4 H5 H6 T1 T2 T3 T4 T5 T6
  (b) HHH HTT THT TTH THH HTH HHT TTT
  (c) A1 A2 A3 B1 B2 B3 C1 C2 C3 D1 D2 D3
  (d) WW WX WY WZ XX XY XZ XW YY YZ YW YX ZZ ZX ZY ZW

6 (a) $\frac{1}{6}$ (b) $\frac{1}{8}$ (c) $\frac{1}{30}$ (d) $\frac{1}{700}$